Little Malice in Blunderland

LITTLE MALICE
IN BLUNDERLAND

Being a not so Fanciful Account of the Adventures of
ALFRED CHATWORTHY, D.D., BISHOP OF BLUNDERLAND

In the Land of Shining Mountains and on
the Rolling Plains of the Great
Northwest during the Early
Reign of the Mass-Man

Compleat with Ridiculosities, Sundry Preachments,
Observations, and Impertinences, Together with
Allegories, Visions, and Aspirations

FOR THE EDIFICATION OF
the Concerned, the Disquieted, and the Curious

Impatiently Assembled and Recorded by the Writer
awaiting in Reasonably Quiet Confidence the
Manifestation of the Spirit in a
Dozing Church

By CHANDLER W. STERLING

Bishop of Montana

With Illustrations by
BOLTE GIBSON

MOREHOUSE-BARLOW CO.
New York

Contents

Dedicated to the vine and olive branches which grow about my door, and to my friends and acquaintances who, in most cases, have made my life most interesting and joyful as well as having made these characters plausible and possible.

Little Malice in Blunderland

"Welcome back, my dear. You still have a home and family, but I am not so sure about the house."

I

No Panther in the Pulpit

FLIGHT 635, Tipwing Airlines, touched down at Hereford City Airport, and with a motored cough stopped in front of the terminal. Alfred Chatworthy, D.D., the Bishop of Blunderland, emerged and waved greeting to his wife and six daughters, the latter truly arrows in the hands of a giant, as Scripture says. While waiting for his luggage, there were hugs and greetings all around, finally to little Julia, reigning from the arms of Kathleen, wife, mother, chauffeur, officer of the day, saint, and martyr.

"My love," saluted Alfred, "it is so good to be back and discover that I still have a home."

"Welcome back, my dear. You still have a home and family, but I'm not so sure about the house."

"Now, what's happened?" asked Alfred, fearing the worst.

"It's not that bad," assured Kathleen, sensing his alarm. "It's just that the hall ceiling fell last week when the water pipe in the front bathroom burst in the middle of the night. The workmen finished yesterday and the older girls and I spent most of today cleaning up their mess."

Alfred paused a moment. "Wonder how much that will cost."

His wife informed him that a bill for $853.09 was on his desk. "Isn't the Diocese supposed to pay it?" she asked hopefully.

"Well, yes," agreed Alfred. "The difficulty lies in the ques-

9

tion of who pays, the Diocesan Executive Council or the Board of Trustees."

"That ought to be very simple," said Kathleen. "The Board of Trustees own the house. It's their problem."

"Yes, I know," replied Alfred, "but the trouble is that the Council receives all the Board's income from the trust funds and pays all the bills."

"Well, so what? Send them the bill."

"My dear, it isn't that simple," he explained. "The Council insists upon having a Committee in Charge of the Maintenance of the Bishop's Residence, but before *they* got around to inspecting the damage and taking action the house could float down to the lake."

"I don't think that's right or fair."

"True, Kathleen, but the Canons of the Diocese have it worked out neatly so that the Council has the authority for everything and I have the responsibility."

"I just don't want you talked into paying the bill yourself."

"With what, buffalo bones or old hymnals?"

Having arrived at the so-called Bishop's palace and given a superficial inspection to the new ceiling and a sidelong glance at the plumbing bill, Alfred began to unpack his suitcase and fill the clothes hamper with two weeks laundry. Daughter Kathy, with the beauty and charm of her mother, and at seventeen showing signs of episcopal deviousness from her father's side, leaned against the door and announced to her stair-bound mother, "Look at all the soiled shirts. Two with soft collars, too. Old 'September Song' has been singing again, I take it."

"Now Kathy, even bishops can't fast and pray all the time," he laughed.

"Tell me, Dad, were you a panther in the pulpit while you were gone?"

"Of course I was, as you well know," he countered, having

a reputation to uphold adding, "It's not hard to be a panther in the pulpit with a puma in the pew."

Mrs. Chatworthy came through the door bearing clean sheets. "There aren't many cougars in the confessional, however," she contributed.

"That's dear old Mom," called Margaret from the bathroom. "Every family should have one medievalist, but we're twice blessed. We have Beth, too." Being a college sophomore, Margaret was the Chatworthy family's contribution to tired humanism, complete with opinions and simple answers to unanswerable questions.

Having repaired to the kitchen, Ann, the high school sprite spoke up. "Daddy, tomorrow is St. Prunella's day. Are you going to have Mass in the Oratory?" She looked at her mother with a sly smile.

The Bishop shuddered. "St. Prunella? Who is she?"

"St. Prunella, virgin, not a martyr," explained the family mystic, Beth.

Alfred thought for a moment. "What a pity. She missed the two great experiences of life."

"What did you say?" challenged Kathleen.

"Tomorrow at seven there will be a celebration of the Holy Communion according to the Book of Common Prayer using the Propers of the Day for the Fourth Sunday after Easter."

"I think we touched a nerve, girls," commented Kathleen to the olive branches as they concluded their cokes.

The phone rang. "It's for you, Daddy," called Sarah.

"How did the news get out so fast that I'm home?"

"Daddy, it's Miss Platen down at the office. She wants to know if you are coming down to answer your mail; it's all piled up on the desk," explained the fifth polished corner of the temple.

The Bishop answered the phone. "Greetings, Miss Platen. You're looking well. All right. I'll be down in about ten min-

11

utes." He hung up and, because it was Harry Perse, the Treasurer of the Diocese, waiting to see him, he picked up the plumbing bill, thinking that he might as well have the preliminary skirmish now. He announced his departure and started walking to the nerve center of the Church in the Diocese of Blunderland, the spiritual wine press of the vineyard, his office.

To his surprise he found Harry in an excellent mood. Word of the fallen ceiling had not reached him yet, obviously. The better news, conveyed by Mr. Perse, was that he had in his possession a check for $637.44, the residue of a small estate, with the instruction that it could be used at the discretion of the Bishop and Council. So, after co-signing the check, Chatworthy sent Harry happily on his way, having decided not to ruin his day by handing him the bill for $853.09, but to spring it on the Council two weeks hence.

Sitting at his desk, the Bishop contemplated the orderly stacks of mail before him and said, "I presume, Miss Platen, that you have separated the good news from the bad, so that I can safely alternate selections?"

Taking a letter from one stack on the desk, the Bishop read that the Rector of St. Laodicea's, Luke Springs, the Reverend Wordsworth Little, desired him to write a foreword to a book of sermons that he was preparing for publication. The letter went on, "It is hoped that this tidy collection of homilies of the day will find a place on every parson's bookshelf."

"So Mr. Little has prepared a book of sermons," reflected Chatworthy. "Every time I visit his parish somebody comes up to me during the coffee hour and asks about one of those Thirty-nine Articles in the back of the Prayer Book. Any congregation that is informed on the Articles of Religion has been forced to find something to read during dull sermons."

The Bishop put the letter aside and reached for another one. *The Witness* magazine has invited him to do a book review; that note was a bit more cheerful. Then to the top of the pile appeared the letter from the Wardens and Vestry at Trinity Church, Bigview, asking the Bishop what he proposed to do about the vacancy there, and could he come down for a meeting.

"That will give me a chance to look over West Concord on the way and see what's left of the church there. I understand that it has been closed for thirty years." he mused.

After dictating several letters the Bishop departed for the house with the new ceiling in the hall. He was met at the door by daughter Ann.

"Daddy, some men were here and left six cases of wine," she reported. "I told them that you would never buy that much, but they said you did, so I told them to put it in the basement. It's all stacked up down there. What are you going to do with all that?"

"I didn't buy any wine, Ann," Alfred said. "My new colleague, the Roman Catholic Bishop of Hereford, is to be consecrated next week. I received an invitation today with a note from him. I'll bet that this shipment is a hopeful gift to His Excellency from the winery."

Ann and Beth followed their father down the basement stairs while he checked the report, and his suspicions. "Sure enough," he announced. "The address is 631, not 531."

Back upstairs, Bishop Chatworthy dialed the chancery office. "Hello. Father Kelly?" inquired Alfred. "Plus Alfred, the Lord Bishop of Blunderland, speaking. May I talk to His imminent Excellency, please?"

"I'm sorry, Bishop, but he is already out mending fences at a reception for him down in Clinkerton. Is there anything that I can do?" explained the assistant.

"Well, Father, I think that I may have the key to a great mystery," offered Chatworthy, relishing what he was up to.

"Don't tell me. Let me guess. You have our champagne for the Consecration reception down at your house!"

"Kelly, you get an 'A'."

"That wasn't hard to figure out, Bishop," replied Father. "I've just finished a long conversation with the delivery man who has been insisting that the champagne had already been left at the bishop's residence. If you are going to be home I'll be right down and pick it up."

"Not so fast, your reverence," Chatworthy teased. "I have a price, mainly because I was honorable enough to call you. You know that my conscience is as well trained as yours."

"All right. What's the ransom?" Kelly asked in mock surrender.

"An audience with the Pope next Fall is all I humbly ask."

"That will be easily arranged, Bishop. Consider the matter taken care of. Just let us know the dates and the necessary arrangements will be made." Father Kelly happily accepted the price.

"A private audience, Father Kelly," taunted Alfred.

"What? With the Vatican Council going on, and all? That will be a little more difficult to arrange."

"Now, Father Kelly, all that I want to do is tell the Holy Father directly what fine fellows you are and what a great job you are doing."

"Right Reverend Sir, you drive a hard bargain. Do I understand that if I will arrange a private audience for you, then I may come down and get *our* own wine?"

"It's a deal, Father, and I look forward to the reception." They hung up with good-natured aves to each other and the Bishop returned to the kitchen.

"And what was that all about, Alfred?" asked Kathleen.

"Just another adventure in ecumenicity, my dear," answered the Bishop.

II

The Bishop and the Moribundant Life

"YOU KNOW, Kathleen," the Right Reverend Alfred Chatworthy remarked, as he finished his second cup of breakfast coffee, "I have been the Bishop of Blunderland for nine months and already I have travelled more in that space of time than St. Paul did in his whole lifetime." He rattled his cup for a refill.

"How did you like the ride, Alfred? And how many times did you say that you had been shipwrecked and endured the lash?" was her rejoinder.

"Well, perhaps I did overstate my heroism a little bit, but I have already been left for dead a couple of times," he replied.

"You're softening me up for something, I can just tell," she probed.

"I was about to announce that I have plans for doing heroic deeds for the kingdom this next week by making a brave foray into a derelict mission area out in the 'left field' of the Diocese. In spite of my fine transportation, to which you have disparagingly alluded, I have not yet visited there," he continued, "and I cannot confess to having heard the Troatic call nor the cry of the penitent."

"Eight hours sleep is too much for you. You're more wordy than ever," was Kathleen's critical rejoinder. "When will you return?" she queried patiently, as she cleared the table.

"Should anyone call, I'll be back in the fall, he said with a drawl," answered Alfred, taking a pleasure in benumbing his wife. "I must go to my hard labor."

"It *would* be a novelty to have *you* in labor for a change," she cut back, as she eyed six empty cereal bowls in the kitchen sink.

Alfred ran up the white flag. "Seriously, my dear, I shall return in a week. Here is my itinerary," he said as he offered her the typed sheet of his daily whereabouts. "Miss Platen has the original so that in case the Diocese burns down I can be notified. I would also like to be called if the Reverend Gerald Flumwell gets that job he has been dickering for. That would really be good news—probably for Gerald, too. He's been through at St. Alonzo's ever since his wife wore that Dutch costume and passed out cheese samples down at the Super-market in Droopington last month. Boy! Did I get the letters on that one!"

The Bishop took his suitcase out to the car and returned to retrieve his brief case and portable typewriter. "Not only per-sonal effects, but a travelling office and sacristy as well," he commented. "And now, my dear, a chaste kiss on the forehead as I wipe the tears from your streaming eyes. . . ."

"Alfred, sometimes I could just . . . ," Kathleen faltered.

"I haven't time to stanch the flow of blood from my wounds, should I loiter around here," he bantered. Then he turned serious. "Call me any time, Kathleen. I'll check in Tuesday for a phone visit, assuming that they don't still de-pend on smoke signals out there."

"Drive carefully, dear. Should anything happen to you now I have too many young children to enter a convent," she said smiling, as they walked to the curb.

"The Lord's on my side," he responded.

"He must be," agreed his wife. "Please keep it that way."

A tank of gas, two doughnuts, and three cups of coffee later he drove into the town of West Concord, nostalgically named by a New Englander beyond hope of ever returning, and the town beyond hope of ever resembling the original.

The town of West Concord was over seventy miles from the nearest traffic light and over two hundred miles from a railroad but was right next to the biggest prairie dog settlement west of the Mississippi. For years it had lived on the bounty of Fort Roberts, an army post, now defunct. The town still lived in the dustiness of past memories, including massacres, and yet cherished the hopeless dream of the day when its future would be restored.

The church had not been in use for twenty-five years. The Bishop drove up and down the dusty, unpaved streets until he found it, safely hidden on a side street. A frame building, dusty white with green trim, a crumbling red brick chimney, powdering, and bending away from the prevailing wind, as the church itself did, in a southeasterly direction. A dead cottonwood tree stood on the corner with its gaunt, whitish limbs clawing at the sky. Ant hills were spotted here and there, identified by five-foot square patches of bare ground. The marks of desolation were completed by the railing which broke off under Alfred's hand as he ascended the church steps.

He tried the key he had brought in the lock, without any confidence that it would work. To his surprise, it turned easily, and he entered. The interior was bare except for some old newspapers, a dozen pews, and a dust-covered pump organ. An old stove, filled with papers and torn hymn books, leaned against a scorched pew.

He noticed that each pew had a small brass plate fastened on the end with legends like these:

To the Glory of God
and in memory of
Capt. E. M. Fawcett—1892

17

In thanksgiving
The Crowther Family
Ft. Roberts—1908

To the Glory of God
in memory of his wife
Joel Barr—1896

The Bishop had been informed that a few years before the missionary last assigned to West Concord had driven over one night and splashed some paint on the outside with the aid of automobile headlights. Alfred verified this in rummaging around. He picked up a receipt for the paint made out to "Dad Haines, Warden, St. Cornelius the Centurian Church, West Concord."

Alfred left this haunting, silent scene of a bygone day and returned to what was the business section of West Concord to find "Dad" Haines, if indeed he were still around. Being a druggist's son, Alfred automatically went to the drugstore. "Gad, it smells good," he thought as he entered. The Bishop was revelling in the mystic aroma when the druggist appeared. Queried about Mr. Haines, he directed Alfred to the Jumble Shop. The Bishop loitered around the store sniffing, and finally, after confessing his boyhood to the pharmacist, went behind the counter and opened bottles to release the forgotten smells of a real, honest-to-goodness drugstore.

Temporarily cheered, he eventually made his way to the second-hand jungle called the Jumble Shop. Alfred looked over and through a forest of dilapidated furniture, bird cages, wicker floor lamps, tea carts and hall trees. Two men were playing cards on an old, round, dining room table in the midst of the musty clutter. The place was cold and smelly, not the pungent, get-well smell of the drugstore, but the smell of death.

The Bishop stumbled over a wire cage rat trap containing a crusted scrap of ancient bread.

"I'm looking for Dad Haines," he called out.

"Yup," was the only answer.

Dad must have been in his late seventies. He had uncut, straggly, white hair and a dirty, grey, beard stubble about two weeks old. Alfred also observed that he had but one ear. Dad constantly wiped at his red-lidded and watering eyes with a soiled handkerchief, holding his cards in his other grimy hand over his sunken-bellied middle. As he looked up, and half-smiled, half-grinned, Alfred detected an occasional part of an occasional, yellow-stained tooth.

His friend, a bejowled old man that looked to the Bishop for all the world like a homesick walrus, having a droopy, tobacco-stained, handlebar mustache, scanned the Bishop from under lizard eyelids, unblinking, cold, and suspicious. Alfred recognized the kind of ring the man was wearing—one of those travelling carnival rings with the figure of a nude woman done in silver against a black background, worn thin with much fingering.

He introduced himself: "I'm Alfred Chatworthy, the new Episcopal Bishop of Blunderland."

"Thought ya was just new here," mumbled Dad. "Ain't seen any other preachers fer quite a spell. Seems I read somethin' about it in the papers, but didn't pay much attention." He paused a moment. "Say, preacher, ain't gonna try and start up the church again, are ya?"

"I don't have any plans at all," answered Alfred. "I'm just getting acquainted and finding my way around. There isn't much left of the church, is there."

"Naw," replied Dad Haines, "most of it's been carried off. Some of the stuff ended up on the reservation. Rest of it was stolen by preachers to put in churches somewhere else—font's down my front yard, if I remember rightly." With a queer

19

smile, Dad looked up slowly at the Bishop, waiting to see how he would take it.

"Why is it down there?" asked Alfred, trying not to show concern.

"Been usin' it fer a bird bath. It's a dandy one, too. All the birds like it. And say," he continued, in a belligerent tone, "I don't want to catch ya takin' that away. All you preachers do is come down here and haul everythin' away to use somewhere else, just as if this town wasn't comin' back."

"As long as this church isn't being used, and there is need for these things elsewhere," continued Alfred, "everything will disappear in time. They really belong to the Diocese, anyway, you know."

"Don't care anythin' about that," Dad muttered as he searched with his foot for a cuspidor. "Just don't want ya takin' my bird bath, that's all . . . What did ya say yer name was? One trouble with getting old; can't remember names."

Dad's friend, the walrus, interrupted, "Women ain't scared or interested in us either." Then, to Dad, "Come on, it's your deal."

"Just a minute," interrupted Haines. "Might as well clear the air around here once and fer all so's he don't get any fancy ideas. We don't want no church here less it be like it was back in Bishop Herrin's time. I just want ya to get that straight." Dad leaned back in his chair and closed his eyes slightly, but was watching the Bishop. "Now *there* was a fella who knew how to run things," he reminisced, as though Alfred were not in the room. "The Bishop'd come here once in a while and announce we'd have church. Sometimes he wouldn't even take up a collection."

"That's because there weren't any men around town with only one arm," snorted the walrus; "he'd a-been lucky to git the plate back with guys like you around."

Dad ignored the comment and returned to the subject of the

"All you preachers do is come down here and haul everythin' away to use somewhere else."

third Bishop of Blunderland. "Yer the new bishop, ya say. Don't get any ideas we're gonna pay anythin'. We ain't never done it and we ain't gonna begin now. There's only four or five of us old timers left around here anyway. When we kick in ya can do as ya please with the old shack, but fer now leave it the way it is," he ordered.

"Do the others feel as you do, Dad? Alfred inquired, barely holding his temper.

"They're too old to care much. Their folks and mine built this here church. We come here as kids to the Fort. Our fathers were all army men. We're just sittin' tight till they open the Fort agin. Dang mistake to ever close it, them wolf-men down in Washington. . . ." The old man began to mellow a bit.

The walrus put down the greasy cards and joined in. "Both Haines and me are 'Piscopals," he explained. "I used to carry the old Bishop's bags in from the stage to the hotel room. I allus figgered that made me 'Piscopal, and so did he, I guess."

"Haw," chuckled Dad, "he was quite a man. Used to sit in the lobby and darn his socks. Nobody dared make any smart remarks. He was the biggest man around, and strong as horseradish. Quiet as a can of worms unless ya got him riled up. Had a voice could be heard five miles in a strong wind," reminisced Dad Haines, shifting into high.

"Those old days are gone forever," philosophized Alfred, who was tiring fast. "Better be on my way. I'll drop in again."

"Ya hadn't better if ya snitch that bird bath," Dad called out as Alfred retraced his trail through the wilderness to the front door.

"You can't hold out forever, Mr. Haines," Alfred called back.

"I kin fer awhile, and I'm plannin' on it."

The Bishop closed the door behind him, took a deep breath of fresh air, and returned to the drugstore. He found a young man there to help him take the font out of Haines' yard. The two of them separated the three sections and put them in the trunk of Alfred's car. "Makes the old bus sit right down like a hot-rod," he observed as he drove the youth back to the drug-store. "I'm tempted to take off the muffler and go all the way," he mused, but wisely reconsidered.

The sign at the edge of town informed the Bishop that it was 137 miles to Broad Ridge, and another 40 to Bigview, where he planned to spend the night.

As one uneventful mile after the other droned by, the Bishop meditated on the day. "That was the saddest example of spiritual impoverishment that I have seen in a long time," he mused. "So many places that I visit have been seeking the Lord on their own terms. Back in the days of the circuit-riding missionary bishops, these people apparently picked up the idea that the Church had mysterious sources of income back East and all that the bishops had to do was go East annually to pick up enough money to keep the Church in the west going. Now if I don't pay for the local operation, I have failed as their leader. One look at Dad Haines and it's easy to believe that the nineteenth-century spectator-Christian is still alive. I'm beginning to get the idea that about all the present-day churchman wants to do is shake the kaleidoscope of the Church in the hope of getting a more pleasant picture. No wonder I'm unpopular in certain circles."

III

The Bishop at Bay

ALFRED ARRIVED in Bigview about nine that evening and made directly for the hotel. After signing in at the desk, he walked up and down Main Street, peering in the store windows, and stopped to pass the time of evening with the manager of the Vogue Theatre, who was standing out in front. He went into Louie's Place for a roll and coffee, both left over from the morning, he suspected. After being looked over and speculated about by the denizens of the booths, something he could not help but notice by the subdued tones of conversation which leaked through the record changes of the juke box, he got up, paid his bill, and, after almost being run down by a jalopy full of Indians, returned to the hotel. The Bishop read himself to sleep by eleven.

The next morning as Alfred was seated on a stool in the restaurant having his breakfast before a propped-up copy of the *Morning Herald,* a well-dressed man in his sixties came up to him and inquired, "Are you the new Bishop from Hereford, by chance?"

Alfred admitted that he was, as he noticed the fine cut of the man's western suit and the weathered roughness of his features.

"Thought I recognized you from the pictures in the paper," he explained. "I'm Gib Morland, one of your strays that holds down one of the nickel seats up at the church. You here to have church?" he ventured.

"I'm just going around getting acquainted, and learning the country," the Bishop answered. "You sure have a lot of room down in this part of the state."

"Say, Bishop," offered Gib, "come on over to the table where we're having our coffee and I'll introduce you around." Alfred carried his cup to the table where three men sat, and was identified all around. A brief silence of self-consciousness followed while the men sized up the Bishop. He was getting used to it, so he broke the ice by saying, "It won't give you heartburn if I sit in, will it?"

Doc Hoefer spoke up, "Heartburn isn't their problem, Bishop. They're just advancing in years and are full of arthritis and cheap whiskey." Doc continued his razzing of his friends. "Teasdale, here, has been drinking 'Old Hammerhandle' for years and still staying on the Board of the Federated Church. That's what I call real diplomacy."

Rex Teasdale ignored the twisting of the knife and diverted the subject. "You know, Doc," said Teasdale, "one guy that had worse manners than you was Harve Bigelow, at least that's the reputation he had; but I can tell a story about him that makes him the inventor of western diplomacy."

Hoefer smilingly let him off the hook, and with the others, nodded for him to drag himself ashore by this diversion. Rex explained to Alfred, "Harve was one of the last of the old cattlemen. He used to get up every morning about four and get his choring done. Then he'd have breakfast and go back to bed. He'd lie there off and on all day, smoking cigars and reading cowboy stories and ranch romances and all that stuff. He never sat in a chair except to eat."

"Harve lasted up into his eighties living like that," put in Jim Rhodes.

"As I was saying," pursued Rex, "late in the afternoon Harve would hoist himself out of bed, do the evening chores, eat his supper, and back to bed he'd go. He'd been doing this for years, and everybody knew about it and paid little attention. Well, one day a cattle buyer from Iowa came to town looking for yearlings and he found out that Harve had some he wanted to take off the range, so he went out to the ranch to talk it over with him.

" 'Mrs. Bigelow' he says, 'is Harvey home?'

" 'Come right in. He's in bed,' she says.

" 'I'm sorry to hear that he's sick. Didn't know.'

" 'He isn't sick. He's just lying there smoking and reading. Go on in,' she invited. 'Harve, man to see you,' she called out.

" 'Hello, Harvey. Thought you were sick, but the Missus says you're just resting.'

" 'Yup,' says Harve. 'What's on your mind?'

" 'Heard in town that you had some yearlings to sell, so I came out to see if we could make a deal.'

" 'Well, now, I think that's just fine,' said Harve. 'Here. I'll turn down the covers. Take off your coat and boots and climb in. Here, have a cigar. Sure glad to have you out to talk business.' "

"That's the way Harve used to sell livestock before the weekly sales days," reflected Gib Morland. "Harve made his money by getting his customers so dang comfortable they gave him all the breaks."

"Wonder if that's where the old saying, 'split the blanket,' came from," speculated Rex.

"Split the blanket means to get a divorce," Jim informed him.

"Yeah, but I'll bet it originally meant any kind of an argument," said Doc.

"Speaking of characters, do any of you remember old Zeb Warner?" asked Gib. "Lived up Deadhorse Draw. He was one for the books."

"I knew him when I was a kid," said Rex. "He used to come

26

to town in a buggy, driving a moth-eaten old nag that was barely able to make it the twenty miles across the valley without falling down. One day Zeb came to town, tight as a barn window. He went down and argued with Ben Baus at the stable trying to beat down his price to keep the horse for two or three days while Zeb stayed likkered up."

"Oh, I remember that," broke in Jim, taking the story away from Rex. "He beat Ben down to where he was only going to charge Zeb a buck for three days to keep the horse. Then Zeb asked Ben to keep the manure to take home. Ben just said, calmlike, that for a buck there wouldn't be any." Everybody laughed, including Alfred.

"Apparently I have survived the first two rounds," assessed the Bishop to himself. He thought that he could see what was coming next.

"Remember that preacher you used to have here, Gib?" reminded Rex. "You know, the Reverend that cut his own hair?"

Gib Morland answered with an embarrassed smile, "He was never too popular from the time he went to Guild Meeting after he'd given himself a bad job. He kept his hat on all through the meeting so it wouldn't show, and the ladies got real upset. He didn't stay around here long enough for me to remember his name. Bishop, we've sure had some dandies," he half-confessed and half-accused.

"Bishop," asked Doc, "how do those guys get into the Church anyhow?"

"About the same way you get some of the Doctors I've met," slyly defended Alfred. Seeing smiles and feeling a little bolder, the Bishop continued, "You know, Doctor, Satan calls as many men to the ministry and to the field of medicine as the Lord does." He paused, waiting for the bomb to go off. There was a short silence.

"That's a new angle. Never thought of it that way," reflected Doc. "But you talk as though you believe in a personal devil. I think that's a lot of medieval nonsense. A person of your training and background should have thrown that out with witchcraft, the bell, book and candle."

"Perhaps so, Doctor," Alfred answered. "It rather embarrasses part of me, too. About all I am prepared to say is that if I reject the idea, then I am disagreeing with a most eminent authority."

"Who's that?" Doc asked, his curiosity rising.

"Our Lord."

"Oh." Silence. Then, "Somebody wrote that in between the lines."

The Bishop spoke up, "I'd just as soon change the subject, too. When I was a boy I used to think that the devil was like Santa Claus—he was only my father."

Everyone laughed easily and with some relief. Alfred always found it interesting to bring up this subject and watch the reaction; there was always a general unwillingness to discuss it, and a genuine uneasiness when there was no getting out of it.

"There are still too many things about the churches which I can't digest," pursued Doc, getting a little bolder himself as he perceived the Bishop's willingness to discuss religious matters calmly.

"Give an example," Alfred suggested.

"Well, people for one thing. Too many frauds and hypocrites cluttering up the place. There's nothing there for me."

The Bishop figured he wouldn't let that old complaint go by unchallenged: "You'll meet some fools and phonies in church, sure, as where won't you? Our Lord had a good right hook for the business contact boys in the churches of His day. Now that you bring up the subject, let's narrow this down a bit and skip the pious fraud who thinks he's impressing God with showy virtues that are really smug vices: he isn't fooling anyone but himself. I believe that we can safely ignore the people who want to keep the lowly in line by feeding them a religion; they get found out when the lowly really turn Christian and learn right from wrong. Sure, you can escape God pretty easily in the Church. As a matter of fact, some people have been doing that for years. It's like getting up close to a wall so that you don't cast a shadow out too far."

Alfred continued, "The Church doesn't really offer any guarantee of ease, comfort, or success. Remember, she has led some of her followers along the road to prison and the stake. The raw meat of the Christian religion has all the comfort of a kick in the teeth."

The Bishop was getting eloquent. "The Church does offer increased knowledge of the universe in which you live—in which you'll always live—by helping you to an understanding of the most important fact in that universe—God. You don't have to believe in a Michaelangelo heaven or a Dante hell to understand that growth and evolution is an unending process, a road which may lead straight ahead or meander and back-track. Some of the Church's road maps may be hazy and generalized, but they are the best available. Sure, a few people are going to read the signs the way they want them to read, but that really doesn't change the maps any."

They were listening intently, the Bishop observed. "There are a lot of men who feel that they don't 'belong' in a church the way that Christianity is organized today. There are others who have a hazy childhood background in religion which either they could not, or did not, continue in adult life. These people have often thought about doing something about it but kept putting it off because they didn't know quite how to go about getting straightened out."

"Brother, you can say that again," broke in Rex.

Alfred stayed at it: "Then there are others of us who can't go along with a cramped, watered down, or sentimentalized religion. We give up trying to find a religion that is realistic and faces life as it has to be lived and can meet the need of the man on the street."

"That's me," spoke up Gib.

"Now don't get any quaint idea that I am trying to 'sell' you the Church. I'm not interested in picking off an individual here and a family there. The Church is interested in having anyone work with us who is trying to untangle his life and bring some sense and order into a confusing world. The Church, if she is doing her business, doesn't want your name, your money, power, or position. She simply wants you to be a part of the dynamic process of God's grace. You'll have to settle your mind on these things some day. That's up to you, not to me."

"Here endeth the First Lesson," intoned Morland.

"And something to think over," said Doc. "Better get up to the office and see who's the sickest." He rose to go, picking up the check.

"Reading those old magazines of yours would give anybody an ulcer or high blood pressure," said Gib. "You doctors are as bad as the preachers. We've either had it, got it, or we're gonna get it. See you later."

After the party had broken up and Gib Morland and the Bishop were going out the door, Gib remarked, "Doc didn't like that, but it did him a lot of good. Gave him something to think about. Let's drive over to the church in my truck," he added as he made for the curb.

Alfred followed Gib Morland around for over an hour as he unlocked the church and escorted him on a tour of the building and the parish hall. The Bishop was then taken on the rounds of the rectory and discovered it to be in the same stage of decrepitude as the house of God.

"Property needs a little work done," observed Morland, "just as soon as you get us a good man." He waited for the Bishop to start making promises.

"I do have a man in mind whom I would like to have look it over," answered Alfred. "I'd want his wife to come with him, too," he added. "It didn't take me long to find out that if a parish can keep a rector's wife happy by providing a comfortable home, then he's likely to stay." The Bishop had started the softening up process on the Warden.

"What do you think we oughta do to make it attractive?" asked Gib. "You know, we aren't used to inviting a man to look us over. All the bishops I ever knew just sent whoever they could get."

"You get to look him over, too. This thing's got to work both ways if we are ever going to have a chance of it working at all," replied the Bishop.

Morland brightened up. "Well, if that's the way we're going to go at it, maybe we better have a Vestry meeting tonight. You're staying over, aren't you?"

"I was planning to," agreed Alfred. Then he added, "It isn't too late to get the news around about having a service tonight, is it?"

"I'll get the women busy on the phone. We oughta do pretty well. Haven't had a service for two months," said Gib. Looking at his watch, he added, "I've got some things that need doing. Why don't you grub around to suit yourself and then come up to the house for dinner?"

The Bishop acknowledged as how he'd like to, declining a ride down to his car. "It's only three blocks. I might make it before I collapse," he said in parting. "See you tonight." He went back into the rectory.

As Alfred wandered from room to room, he made mental notes of what he would present to the Vestry. "Let's see," he ruminated, "if this parlor doorway is removed, then they would have a bigger living room. Outside of that a complete redecorating job ought to do it . . . There are three bedrooms. That would be big enough for Goodrich and his family, if I can get him." He made his way to the kitchen. One look around told him that this part of the job was going to be expensive. The sink with the pump on the drain board would have to go, and a double sink put in, "and I'll plug for a disposal, too. There might be a plumber on the Vestry." He paced about silently until he spied an old icebox on the back porch. "That has to go," he resolved, "and that stove, too. I could just hear Kathleen if she ever came in here." Alfred decided that he would include a new floor for the kitchen and

"The sink with the pump on the drain board would have to go."

a shower installation in the bathroom with the other improvements and try to get all this by the Vestry that night.

The Bishop returned to the church. His second look at it was depressing. One gothic window was completely gone and had a mattress carton cut to fit the frame. The light fixtures were old-fashioned "bug-catchers." "God must be an absentee landlord around here," he thought, as he noticed the dust covers on the sanctuary furniture. The two altar candles, bowed by the summer heat of a month ago, doubled against themselves, resting their tops on the altar. He went into the sacristy. It was a closet with a window, a folding table, and a full-length metal cabinet with a bent leg. He noticed a quorum of boxelder bugs around the sill.

"This job is not only a 'challenge' but an assignment for a general handy man," Alfred decided. "Now if I can persuade Goodrich to give this place a consideration, I could tell him that if he will take this place and put it in order I'll nominate him for Grace Church, Ardmore, when Dr. Codger vacates . . . let's see, Sewickley retires in four years; that would be about right."

Pleased with himself, the Bishop returned to his room at the hotel, preparatory to an afternoon of calling. There was a note at the desk asking him to visit the hospital and call on old Mrs. Tompkins in 214. There was also another message, "Soonazee cumzin call Missus Huckleby." He observed that the barbed-wire telephone was in good working order here in Bigview. During the afternoon he made his appointed rounds and presented himself at the Morlands for dinner at six o'clock.

Gib chewed on his cigar and fidgeted in his chair while the two of them were waiting for dinner. Finally Morland confessed, "Bishop, I usually have a snort of Old Popskull before dinner. You came in the front door as I came in the back and I haven't had mine. Will you join me?"

"Well, if it's anything like Old Hammerhandle that they

were talking about this morning, you'd better put some water in it for me," acquiesced Alfred.

"This stuff isn't prairie lightning, Bishop," explained Gib. "Doc says you shouldn't touch the stuff until you're forty and then never be without it. It'd be safe in your hands, I think." The Bishop made no comment.

The Vestry meeting was called for 9:00 P.M., right after the service, and was held in the Board of Directors' Room of the Bigview National Bank. When everyone had assembled and Chester Brooks, the President of the Bank, had locked the outer door to exclude any late customers, Gib called the meeting to order and turned it over to the Bishop.

"Gentlemen," the Bishop began, as he quickly attempted to identify each vestryman in the role that Alfred expected him to play in the forthcoming debate, "it is a genuine pleasure to meet with you tonight. I've had a pleasant day of it here in Bigview, climaxed by a superb dinner at the Morlands' home. I welcome the opportunity to discuss the future of Trinity, Bigview." He paused, waiting for everyone to get their guard down, and then continued, "I think that I can get the right man for you." There was no reaction whatever to the declaration. The Bishop proceeded. "I am going to send the Reverend Ralph Goodrich here for an interview. I also have a couple of other candidates in mind, but I would like to have you look over this fellow first." The Bishop admitted to himself that he was managing the truth just a little, but it had the desired effect.

"You mean you're going to send a man here for us to look over?" Clyde Long demanded, as though he couldn't believe it.

"It works both ways, Clyde. He'll do some looking over, too," Alfred replied.

Chester Brooks came up on the idea like a mouse approaching a set and loaded trap. "Who's going to pay his expenses for this trip?" he inquired suspiciously.

"I'll split it with you men," volunteered the Bishop.

"Wait a minute, fellows," interposed Tim Whaley. "I'd like to hash it over a little bit. I'm in favor of all this, but we're going to have to work out some details and make some plans for all this. The Bishop is being more than fair on this deal, but we sure gotta make up our minds about some things if we're gonna get looked over, too."

"Yup," agreed August Riemenschneider. "He'll want to look at that rectory and that'll be the last we'll see of that fellow."

The Bishop continued with the "soft sell." "Men, I spent quite a bit of time up there today, and I think that if you make a few basic improvements in the kitchen, and redecorate, you can get out with a presentable improvement without too much cost. I know that you are financially low with this extended vacancy, and all. Goodrich can help you correct that in short order. But first we've got to fix up the house so that he can keep his wife happy."

Everyone laughed, some uncomfortably, and waited for the Bishop to continue. The Bishop didn't. He waited for them.

Dr. Carroll started the ball rolling. "I understand that the Junior Warden is in charge of buildings and grounds, technically, anyway. I move that we put in a new sink, a stove that works and get a new floor in the kitchen."

"Second the motion," said Whaley.

August broke in. "We gotta do something about a refrigerator. If he gets a look at the icebox, we'll never get him or anybody."

The Doctor added that the bathroom needed to be modernized.

"Where we going to get the money to pay for all this?" asked Chester Brooks, turning to the Bishop.

Alfred met this one head-on. "Why, Chester, the property here is worth about $40,000, and there isn't any money owed on it. Do you suppose the bank would give us a note to do the work, at maybe 4½%?"

"Money's pretty tight, Bishop," excused Chester.

Clyde Long, who had been silent through all this, raised another question. "How much are we going to offer this fellow? We'd better start thinking about that one, too."

The Bishop answered quickly, "I'd say start him at $4500, house, heat, utilities, and pension."

The lightning had struck. There was a dead silence, then the thunder.

"We paid that last man only $3600," put in Whaley.

"Yeah. And how long did he stay?" retorted Clyde. "He couldn't afford it when his teeth started falling out with the diet he was on with that income."

"It wasn't that bad, Clyde," excused Gus Riemenschneider.

"Well," added the Bishop, "would any of you men work for that?"

Silence.

"That's right, Bishop, but where are we going to get the money?" defended Brooks.

"Now, I've been looking over a few matters here," began Alfred. "You have eighty-two pledges which total $2460 a year—that's only thirty dollars a pledge. If the parish tripled that you could make it easily."

"Triple it! Now, Bishop, our people can't afford that!" expostulated Brooks.

"Chester, you know better than that," Alfred remonstrated. "You are in a position here at the bank to know what the incomes are in the community, and the people can well afford it." There was a sag in the debate for a moment. The Bishop continued. "Here's what I'll do. You get these pledges up where they ought to be; they haven't changed here since 1939, and everybody's waiting for you to put on the heat, anyway. All I have to do is certify that I can come up with a man that's worth it, and will work with you to get this property in shape, restore the church, make it a force in the community, and all that. If you will offer him $4000 and promise him a 25% share of the increase in giving after six months, I think we can get him." As an afterthought, the Bishop said, "I will make up the difference for the six months. This means, of course, that your apportionment to the Diocese would have to be paid regularly."

That brought an end to the debate, and after a few minutes the plans were completed for rectory repairs and for inviting the Reverend and Mrs. Ralph Goodrich to Bigview for an interview.

As Clyde Long and Gus Riemenschneider were driving home after the meeting, Gus remarked, "You know, Clyde, I kinda think that the Bishop picked up all the marbles tonight."

"Yeah, and did you see the look on Chester's face when the Bishop called him on that income business? He was holding out for 6% on a loan and a subsidy from the Diocese." Clyde laughed long.

After the meeting the Bishop went to Dr. Carroll's home with Morland, the Senior Warden. "Thanks, Doctor, for coming through on the repairs," said Alfred.

"Always get my cues, if not from the patient, from the doctor," he replied, engaged in hanging up coats and affecting indifference.

Late that night, as Alfred made his third and final turn on to his back, he reflected, "Praise God, I can still sleep like a saint, rejoicing in my bed, in spite of the fact that I suspect that being a bishop is forcing me to develop the tactics of a high pressure salesman." He yawned, stretched, gave a mighty sigh, and fell asleep.

IV

What Really Happened to J. Walter Tarp?

BACK IN HIS OFFICE several days later, the Bishop of Blunderland swung around in his swivel chair and once more faced the earnest Reverend J. Walter Tarp (Kenosis Seminary, B.D. '64). The conventional niceties of inquiring into the nature of each other's health and respective families had been dutifully observed, and all of its possibilities exhausted.

"Well, Tarp," resumed the Bishop, "after much prayerful consideration I have decided to appoint you Vicar of St. Lethargus' Mission at Sunken Heights. You should regard this as a real challenge, to which I trust you will respond." Tarp nodded. "Unfortunately there has been a succession of clergymen there, sixty-three in sixty-five years, to be exact. I would like to have you break the record and stay for three years. Things were going along well during the sixteen months that Father Censable was there. It was indeed unfortunate for the congregation that he accepted a call to 'a wider field of service' before he really got started. However, in the past year, until the Rev. Mr. Scarph received appointment to that strategic post in the Diocese of Metropole, St. Lethargus' gave every indication of coming into its own. This year they celebrate their sixty-fifth year as a Mission, and there is a good spirit there. The Warden himself told me that they expect to pay their Diocesan Assessment in full this year, and will try to pay part of their Apportionment as well. So, young man, I am

"Unfortunately there has been a succession of clergymen there, sixty-three in sixty-five years, to be exact."

counting on you to rally the people and make great strides for the Kingdom."

With these words, the interview came to an end.

The arrival of the Tarp family in Sunken Heights was marked by a reception on Wednesday evening following his first Sunday service, and was heralded by the Sunken Heights *Evening News* announcement of "The Reverend Tarp's" entry into the religious and social life of the community. Everyone was genuinely pleased to meet and greet the new Vicar and his lovely wife, and they did hope that he would stay, for he seemed to be such a fine young man. The Methodist and Congregational ministers, who were present at the reception, thought so, too.

For the next several weeks, everything went along exceedingly well. He seemed, indeed, to satisfy all factions in the congregation. Those who had been offended by Fr. Censable (who preferred Holy Communion to Morning Prayer), and by Mr. Scarph (who preferred Morning Prayer to Holy Communion), returned to the fold and joined the faithful each Sunday, and even withdrew their children from the Lutheran Sunday School. Soon the church was filled every Sunday, and on Christmas Eve folding chairs had to be carried in from the Guild Hall. For the first time in eight years, there were acolytes at all services, and on the Saturday before Easter, there were seventeen Baptisms!

At the Mission Board meeting on the second Monday after Easter (which didn't meet until nine o'clock because of the Chamber of Commerce Banquet), it was voted to pay the Diocesan Assessment in full through April. Furthermore, it was moved that the Vicar be given a twenty-five dollar a month raise, provided that the Diocesan Council would not deduct that amount from their share of the support of the work at St. Lethargus'. There was a final motion that a rubber mat be purchased for the front step to the church with "Welcome" stamped on it, to announce the cordial warmth and good will of the oldest church in town. Harry Miterbox, proprietor of the hardware store, interrupted proceedings to announce that it would be a gift. The meeting adjourned amidst a sea of good feeling.

During the winter months, the Reverend J. Walter Tarp had been successful in getting some of the men to give of their time and talent in the evening to renovate the Guild Hall and refinish the Bishop's Chair. The ladies of the Guild caught the spirit, putting up new curtains and purchasing a new second-hand refrigerator to go with the hot plate that they bought a year ago in time for the Shrove Tuesday Pancake Supper. Everyone was genuinely happy. "He is such a fine young man," they said to each other, "and he has such a lovely wife. I do hope that they will stay."

On the last Sunday in May, the Bishop came for Confirmation. Both he and the congregation were surprised by the size of the class. There were eleven children and eight adults, including the new manager of the National Pickaxe Company, who with his wife, were lapsed Methodists from Milwaukee. A few members of the congregation were startled to see "Dice" Lushwell in the class, along with his wife, whose mother was on the Altar Guild. (Dice was bartender on weekends at the Buffalo Club, and was otherwise employed as a used car salesman during the week.) Any apprehension, however, was quickly dissipated by the over-all happiness of the occasion. The Bishop was both strengthened and relieved by the assurance of Mr. Sitwell, the Vice-President of the First National Bank, who fairly beamed when he declared, "This young man is a fine young man, and he has such a lovely wife, and we all do hope that he will stay, Bishop."

There was some concern expressed at the July meeting of the Mission Board over their financial ability to get through the summer. And would the Vicar please explain why he is unwilling to count his two weeks at Church Camp as part of his vacation. And, oh yes, did the Vicar really feel that it was necessary to join the Volunteer Fire Department? Everybody knows what goes on at their barbecue feeds, and it may not be wise to be seen with them too often. Then Harvey Quiverlip, the Clerk of the Board, said that he didn't want to be critical but his wife was quite upset because she heard that Mrs. Tarp hadn't called on Mrs. Grundy since before Easter, and we got to handle her with kid gloves because she might leave the church something in her will, and you can't be too careful because we wouldn't want anything to happen. The meeting was adjourned on a strained and apprehensive note.

Nothing came of it right away because some of the larger pledgers got together at the Pine Cone Cafe and paid up for the year in advance, and it looked as though everything would go along all right until the Every Member Canvass. Then, J. Walter ran into considerable difficulty in getting Sunday School teachers, and, when September rolled around, teachers were still needed for the sixth grade boys and the eighth grade girls, as well as two more in the Primary Department, and there was no one to take over the Little Helpers and keep the pink and blue ribboned Cradle Roll up-to-date.

Church attendance had not picked up by the middle of October and the Vicar was criticized for selecting unfamiliar hymns and spending too much time at the Corner Drug. Matters came to a head a few days later, when it was learned that the Reverend J. Walter Tarp had privately baptized Charlie Cornstubble, who operated the Livestock Rendering Works, along with his wife and six children, and that she was helping in the Primary Department. Fast on the heels of such disconcerting news, followed the word that the Vicar was seen coming out of the Buffalo Club last Saturday holding up Jim Corker, who had had one more drink than he needed, getting him into a car, and driving him home. The Van Scroogies had already begun to attend the Congregational church again, and the Harplong family had cancelled their pledge ($39.00 a year).

Along with these fast moving events, there appeared a classified ad in a national Church magazine:

> POSITION WANTED: Experienced priest, Prayer Book Churchman, seeks correspondence with Vestries looking for aggressive Rector. Good administrator, able preacher, teacher, youth work. Salary secondary consideration. Reply Box T-734.

On Epiphany Sunday, the Reverend J. Walter Tarp announced to his congregation, that, after prayerful consideration, he had accepted a call to become Rector of St. Martha's-at-the-end-of-the-Rope in the Diocese of Amazonia. On the same Sunday, eight hundred miles away, the Lay Reader-in-Charge at St. Martha's made a similar announcement, and everyone there was cheered when informed that he was a fine young man and that he had a lovely wife and "we all hope that he will stay."

The following week, the Bishop received a letter from the Wardens and Mission Board of St. Lethargus', Sunken Heights, that the Reverend J. Walter Tarp had terminated his services, and did the Bishop have anyone in mind to succeed him, and who is going to take the services in the meantime?

So began St. Lethargus' sixty-sixth year as a mission congregation in the Diocese of Blunderland.

V

Chatworthy Versus the Halls of Learning

THE BISHOP leaned back in his chair and opened the bottom left-hand drawer of his desk to provide a foot lever for tipping backwards. Glancing again at the imposing picture of the first Bishop of Blunderland, he set himself to complete the day's dictation. "One more letter, Miss Platen," Alfred Chatworthy went on, "to the Bishop of Latitude, 666 Vacuous Vista Drive, Broadsburg, Pensadormia. Dear Bishop. . . ." Alfred fought off an impulse to remind Penelope Platen of his excellent memory for things that he could afford to forget. His gaze returned to the penguin-attired nineteenth-century apostle who was staring down on him from the wall as if he did not approve of his successor.

Miss Platen broke his momentary fixation on the portrait. "I confess that there are times when I doubt if Bishop Warrier would approve of either one of us. He looks so grim."

"Could be one of two reasons for it," ventured Chatworthy. "Either he is holding in a set of loose dentures or fighting for the Faith. Naturally I prefer to believe the latter. We must get on. . . .

"Dear Bishop: Enclosed is the Letter Dimissory for the Reverend J. Walter Tarp. Fr. Tarp is an excellent young priest. He is leaving his charge, not because he failed in his work, but rather because he has not yet succeeded. Although he was a recent graduate from Kenosis Seminary, there were certain obvious gaps in his training that made it most difficult for him to cope with situations in an isolated field, where he could not rely on a neighboring priest. I have every confidence that he will take advantage of his new associations among the clergy brethren and avail himself of the opportunities for further reading by frequenting the library at Nebula Divinity School. When a young priest is left to himself, as is so often the case in this area of great distances, and has had insufficient academic and spiritual training, it becomes a great trial to both himself and the Bishop, as well as to the people. At any rate Walter flounders well, and with proper care and feeding, a fine priest can be made of him."

"I don't like to see him go, Bishop," sympathized Miss Platen. "He was a fine young man, and he had such a lovely wife. I was hoping that he would stay."

"J. Walter had to leave, Penelope. The congregation chased him up a tree six months after he arrived. Why? He didn't know the strength of the Enemy. Walter had a magazine digest education and he ran out of fuel." Alfred carefully closed the lower drawer of the desk and started putting on his coat and hat. "The day is coming when I shall regret that I let Tarp go. If there had been some way for him to have been placed closer to a wise and learned priest to compensate for his spotty education, perhaps I could have kept him. But out there at Sunken Heights he just did not have the spiritual or moral stamina to survive alone for very long."

"The Examining Chaplins are waiting for you over at the Cathedral," reminded his secretary.

"I am not quite finished with the subject, Miss Platen," ignored Chatworthy. "Young men like J. Walter know all about Kierkegaard but they have never heard of Kirk or a Kempis. They can expound on Tillich by the yard, but they're all vague about Tertullian and Thomas Aquinas. Hooker can't be identified, but everyone knows Henry the Eighth. Harnack and Harton might be a soap firm for all they know. These fellows remind me of a Hollywood movie set when they arrive fresh from seminary for their canonicals—a neat, fenced-in front yard, with a contemporary split-level-structure, but nothing underground or upstairs, and when you open the door, you look out into the weeds. They have the *bon mot,* but not the Good Word—if you get what I mean."

The Bishop announced that he would return late in the afternoon to sign the letters and that now he was going to St. Angus' to see if the candidates were prepared "with all faithful diligence, to banish and drive away from the Church all erroneous and strange doctrines contrary to God's Word."

Alfred enjoyed the five-block walk to the Cathedral on these bright mornings. He fell to humming,

> As sometimes it may happen,
>   That a victim may be found,
>   I've got a little list,
>   I've got a little list,
> Of society's offenders
>   Who might well be underground,
>   And never would be missed. . . .
>   And they're sent to hear sermons
>   From mystical Germans
> Who preach from ten 'til four. . . ."

"Good morning, Excellency," cheerily called Ovid O'Shaughnessy from the Motor Harbor Service Station, "and what is the state of the Church today?"

"Greetings to you, Ovid," replied Alfred. "While I cannot speak for the state of affairs across the Tiber, I can honestly report that today we examine the young men for Holy Orders."

"You mean like being put under discipline?" questioned Ovid.

"Not quite. It is I that will go under discipline today, my friend," quipped Chatworthy, smiling.

"Never could figure you 'episcolopians' out," complained the Seer of Sage Street, "you got different words for everything."

"So we have," agreed Alfred, "and some different ideas, too." The Bishop resumed his walk toward St. Angus', and Ovid disappeared under a car on the grease rack.

Upon entering the Cathedral House, he could hear the industrious clack of typewriters in an adjoining room as the candidates were transferring their learning to paper. A handshake all around and exchange of greetings with the Examining Chaplains followed in the Dean's study as Alfred put his hat and coat on the antiquated Bishop's chair that he had caused to be removed from the Cathedral sanctuary. (The 'oak maiden,' he called it.) The examiners were busy reading the papers that had already been turned out from the teeming brains and smoking typewriters of the aspiring and perspiring candidates in the adjoining room. He was handed a paper fresh from the young mind of Edgar Beaver, Pabulum '66.

"Hope the new heresy doesn't upset you, Bishop," remarked the Reverend Felix Filio from behind a pile of papers.

"It is not the uniqueness, Felix, it's the incredibility that gets me sometimes," replied Chatworthy. Then he sat in silence, reading the new learning, the *Novum Organum Ex Pabulum*.

"Gentlemen, listen to this," announced Fr. Trent. (He was Rector of St. Chalcedon's at Macedon City.) "I quote: 'It is an extraordinary fact that scholars have been so bemused by medieval theories, long since disproved by science, concerning such childish fancies as the efficacy of prayer and the miracles, that they have not perceived that we have in this passage nothing less than the key to the origin of the so-called Lord's Supper.' "

"At last! The leader from Olympus to bring us from darkness into light. Which one of them gives us this insight, Chauncey?" sardonically asked the Reverend Major Cornelius from St. Centurion's, Ft. Maginot.

47

"Hope the new heresy doesn't upset you, Bishop."

"Ronald Whatgift, Lacrima Seminary," informed Fr. Trent.

"Sounds like Professor Medley," reflected Father Filio. "This is one of those situations where a key course is being taught by a recent convert to the Church who never attended any seminary. I have met him. He doesn't show the slightest interest in even examining the Faith of the Church."

"He is the one who stresses that no one really understood the cardinal tenets of the Christian Religion until the nineteenth century," explained the Bishop. "He isn't sure that the Book of Acts has been written yet."

"Ha! Listen to this!" announced the Reverend Hugo Victor of St. Champia's, Clearview. "The so-called Gospel of pseudo-Mark cannot be put earlier than the year 300. The Epistle to the Romans, a hopelessly confused collection of fragments consisting mostly of translations from Egyptian magical incantations, we put at 650 A.D. There are some so-called Early Church Fathers who purport to quote these books but sound scholarship has now agreed that they are nothing but a mass of forgeries."

"There is nothing worse than the kind of ignorance that regards itself as being wise," quoted Chatworthy from something he had read.

"I see by this paper of Bradford MacNail that our Lord wrote the Mass in Latin on Maundy Thursday afternoon," reported Fr. Filio.

"Crazy mixed-up kid," commented Cornelius.

"Professors are on the run from Truth, too," observed Hugo Victor.

Through the rest of the morning the guardians of the Faith sat reading and commenting occasionally when some new insight was revealed. When the lunch hour finally arrived, the Chaplains were groggy, and the Candidates glazed and zombied from their efforts to regurgitate the new learning.

As they reconvened for the afternoon, no one seemed eager to get back to reading the tests which were rolling off the

49

typewriters. After a melancholy and preoccupied silence, Fr. Trent spoke. "Bishop, at the Provincial meeting of Examining Chaplains last winter, we discussed one problem at length. I learned that in some of our seminaries, textbooks from the denominations are substituted for Anglican materials in courses on doctrine. The Pedestria School of Theology does this consistently—probably the only thing they do consistently."

"So I have been informed, Chauncey," answered Chatworthy. "That is why I do not send men there. I have to have as much assurance as possible that my men will come out of seminary theologically literate. At least I expect the seminaries to give them all that they can hold that is relative to the Faith."

"Bishop," rejoined Hugo Victor, "we have all received copies of the Bibliography of Theological Studies and Examinations prepared by the Joint Commission on Theological Education. It seems comprehensive enough to me."

"And so it is, Victor," replied Chatworthy, "but nothing is done to require its use. There are always some professors who think that they know better."

Apparently sensing a feeling of inability to meet the situation, the Chairman, Fr. Trent, broke in. "Gentlemen, I shall call them in for some oral examination. They probably have typer's thumb by now anyway."

Into the room trooped five young candidates looking as if they were appearing for a police line-up. The Bishop tried to put them at ease: "Please sit down, men. We are going to save time for both of us by asking you to discuss some of the questions with us." The men uncomfortably found places, feeling that their backs were literally up against the wall. Fr. Filio looked straight ahead, austerely. Dr. Cornelius lit on his pipe, as Hugo Victor tried to relax the tension by remarking on the fall-out of such a deadly weapon.

Fr. Trent began the questioning: "Mr. Whatgift. . . ."

Ronald Whatgift stiffened perceptibly as he heard the bell toll for him. The Candidate managed a sickly smile and

Trent continued, "Would you please explain briefly what happened to the human race that made necessary the Incarnation?"

Whatgift rubbed his hands together, thought a moment, and finally replied that he did not understand the question.

"Ron," the Bishop interposed, "Fr. Trent means Original Sin. Just tell us how you expect to teach it to your people."

"Oh, Bishop," answered Whatgift, "The Genesis myth has no place in the faith of today."

"I admit that it doesn't seem to, sir, judging from the general lack of information that is current about it in the world today," replied Chatworthy. He paused for a moment and then quietly asked, "What, then, is the Incarnation all about?"

"That has something to do with the divinity of Christ, I believe," suggested Whatgift.

"It most certainly does, young man," exploded Fr. Filio. "Are you trying to tell us that you don't understand the doctrine or that you reject it?" he demanded.

"Neither one, sir," said Whatgift, taken aback by Fr. Filio's attack. "I am trying to answer directly, but this material was covered in an elective—to fill out the course, you know—and I am trying to recall what Tillich said about it. . . ."

"Let it ride for the moment, Whatgift, and let's go into another field." Filio furrowed his brow, pulled himself up and pressed again, "Does a person have to be baptized to be a Christian?"

"That, sir, depends on what a Christian is. Kierkegaard said, and I quote, 'The only true Christian was Jesus Christ'; therefore, it is most difficult to answer your question."

"Difficult to ask them, too, if I expect an answer that makes sense," snorted Filio.

51

Chatworthy, as persistent as the all-state tackle at the Junior Prom, went doggedly back to the first question. He was in one of his patient-paternal attacks. "Gentlemen. The other night on TV during the fights the announcer interviewed a boxer of many years' experience who was still fighting. This man, whose name I can't remember, made what may go down in history as the wisest observation of anybody in the twentieth century, seminary professors included. This pugilist said, 'Man, you don't learn nothing 'til you're tired.' " Alfred paused for a moment and decided that everyone was with him, so far, but obviously puzzled at his meaning.

He continued. "Some years ago a theologian stated that history is the record of man exhausting his desire to be independent of God. Would any of you young men like to make a comment on those two statements, perhaps relating them to the Church's doctrine of Original Sin?"

Silence. A shaking of heads. The Bishop had hit the bottom of the well with a full bucket and not one of them got wet from it.

Chatworthy drew their attention from Whatgift for a moment by putting a question to Edgar Beaver. "Young man, how do you intend to explain the Christian teaching on death and eternal life to your people?"

Beaver quickly replied, "There are some appealing things in Poole's book about Paul's Judeo-Christian concepts of death on which he elaborates by taking the whole subject out of the time-space continuum. . . ."

"That puts us all up in the air, doesn't it?" observed Fr. Trent. "Run that through again, Beaver. That's new to us old fogies."

Beaver floundered well, the Bishop observed, but much like Tarp. Three years in seminary had done him in—temporarily, he hoped. Chatworthy moved back into the situation, annoyed but controlled. "Gentlemen, with keen insight, the first and one of the greatest of our bishops, Samuel Seabury, in case you've forgotten, made a statement about innovations: 'The faith and doctrine of the Church is tried and settled. We have a right to examine what it is, but we must take it as it is.' Thus far today we have not even been able to determine what the faith and doctrine is. You have been busy all day remodeling the sacraments and the creeds. When we do that, it is not Christ's Church, but *our* church, and would remain so, call it what you please."

Two hours passed before the Examining Chaplains and the Bishop could stop the leaks in the Ark. They finally adjourned for dinner and a relaxed evening together, a bit battle-worn and frustrated, a little tired, a little older—and considerably irritated.

"I doubt if they will get Hall, Kirk, Moss, Moberly, and Gore read and digested by tomorrow, but at least *we* will get a respite," remarked the Bishop, as he pushed back from the table at the Antelope Club and lit a cigar.

"Bishop, you should have seen the look on your face when Bradford MacNail answered Filio's question on *ex opere operato* by guessing that it had something to do with sick communions for surgical patients," roared Dr. Cornelius.

"I couldn't help thinking," remarked Chatworthy, "about my visitations among our clergy; present company excepted, I have only found seven priests out of forty who are readers."

"I have been in several rectories," volunteered Hugo Victor, "and have sneaked a look at some rather pathetic libraries. I suspect that many of our clergy have been discouraged from reading by the assignments that were given to them in seminary. A man can stand only so much vapidity, and then he gives up the whole idea of learning as a bad job, and, in this case, before he realizes that Anglican thinkers and writers down through the years have something to say, and that they say it better than most."

" 'How to escape God in the Church' could well be taught by some of these instructors," commented Fr. Filion.

"They teach it by example already," added Dr. Cornelius.

"Bishop," offered Fr. Trent, "let's meet back at the Cathedral and work out a resolution to present to all the Examining Chaplains in the Province, and then have you present it to the next meeting of the House of Bishops."

"Like what?" tentatively probed Alfred.

Fr. Trent continued. "We need a positive statement about the relationship between Church Seminaries and the Church, and the responsibility of the Seminaries to the Church."

"I will if you will," cautiously volunteered the Bishop.

"We should send a report to each Seminary, describing in lurid detail how each man fell on his face, in turn, during his examinations," added Dr. Cornelius.

Fr. Hugo Victor voiced an observation, "I think that we should inquire why today's graduate cannot make a clear cut, three-way distinction between Rome, Canterbury, and Geneva."

"Remember when the Bishop had that Roman Catholic priest out for a clergy conference and went over the whole matter?" recalled Fr. Filio. "Even Alaric Donebetter and E. Sewickley Codger regarded the lectures as sheer inspiration."

"Most of our trouble, gentlemen, comes from usually just one man per faculty," explained Chatworthy. "For instance, that man Flabberly teaching at Nebula. He is from the Church of the Revised Covenant—the same background as the Apologetics man from Wackleff now at Kenosis Seminary." He went on, "An analysis of required and recommended reading will have to be made by the Joint Commission, and then the bishops will have to put it into operation. I believe that the Commission has done an excellent job so far, but it has no authority to put teeth into its recommendations. I think that it's up to us to be noisy about our problems of examining men prior to Ordination."

"Bishop," smiled Dr. Cornelius, "I can just see these young men being questioned at Ordination about obeying the godly admonitions of the Bishop, and their replying instead from the Order for Holy Baptism, 'I renounce them all and promise not to follow or be led by them . . .' Ha!"

"Let us depart in peace, gentlemen," announced Alfred.

"That is obviously a scholastic forgery of the fourteenth century, your Lordship," mimicked Trent.

VI

Celebrating at the City Dump

THE RED FLASHER light on the patrol car reflected in the rear-view mirror of the Eocene 6, Bishop Chatworthy's eight-year-old mechanical marvel. He politely pulled over to the curb, rolled down the window, and resignedly awaited the arrival of the law.

"Good morning, Noah," he cheerfully greeted the officer.

"Good morning, Excellency. Seems like here we are again, and you without that muffler replaced."

"You might explain to the chief that it isn't a bit noisier than that siren on the patrol car, or that horn on the diesel freight that awakens all Christendom every morning at three-twenty," stalled Alfred.

"That is beside the point, sir. This car is becoming a public menace, no personal offence intended, Bishop. It was only this morning that the Captain said to us troopers, 'Now, men, go out and pull in every offender that you find, and do a good day's work for the state, and for the forces of law and order.' So I go out to do my duty, and who do you suppose comes along first? You, Excellency." He wore a suffering and embarrassed look. "Now you go to the garage and get that muffler replaced and there won't be a ticket. But take it easy on us troopers."

The Bishop roared down the street and pulled in to Ovid O'Shaughnessy's Motor Harbor. He walked from there to his office, recalling what he had read about mufflers now being

56

part of the planned obsolescence of the Detroit chariot makers, and that he was being forced into supporting the economy by regularly buying new mufflers to maintain prosperity, as if everyone were in the muffler business.

" 'Morning, Miss Platen," he abruptly greeted his secretary, and walked straight to his desk.

Sensing that something had happened between the breakfast table and the office door, she asked probingly, "Feel all right this morning?"

"Yes, yes, I feel all right, but I'm being hounded by the minions of law and order, who are baying at my heels just because I haven't replaced the muffler on the Eocene," he complained loudly.

"I think the whole machine ought to be replaced. It's a disgraceful pile of junk, that's what it is," observed Miss Platen as she placed the mail on the desk.

"My daughter won two drag races on the airport strip with it last week. It has a lot of miles left in it. I will give it up only on condition that Mrs. Sitwell, who objects to it more than anyone else, arranges for a new Belchfire 8 to replace it." Chatworthy was being difficult. "The whole trouble is that everyone is trying to get me to improve my status symbol. Great Scott, woman, that jalopy *is* my status symbol! I love to park it in front of a big church, give the keys to an acolyte and have him warm it up for me, just to upset the Sitwells of this world. It's good for my soul, and theirs, too." Alfred was sidetracked from his oration when he noticed the letter on the top of the pile. It was written in pencil on brown paper and was a brief note:

Dear Mr. Bishop:

Can you come to Bigpine country for Chrismas service? We fix up schedule for church all over Dec. 24-25. Inform people at Bigview. White people there embarrass to ask. Not so Joe. Hope you come. Big party on the night with ice cream pants.

The last line puzzled Alfred, but by then he had already decided to take services throughout that area during the holidays.

So it was that the Bishop of Blunderland departed home and see city the day before Christmas. Driving the Eocene 6 over four hundred miles with a new muffler, however, took some of the pleasure out of the long trip. In due season Alfred arrived at Bigview and checked into the hotel; he found a note awaiting him at the registration desk: "Bury baby at Red Shirt Table in afternoon? Everybody there soon."

The Bishop did not even go to his room, but went directly to the car to drive the sixty-five additional miles over back roads until he came to a grouping of autos of more ancient make than his. There were a half dozen wagons drawn up in a half circle as well, standing on top of the treeless hill. Chief Bartholomew greeted the Bishop and told him the particulars. Alfred put on his vestments, leaning into the wind. "Elizabethan vestments weren't made to be worn at prairie funerals," he mused as he joined the silent gathering.

The tiny wooden box was lifted out of the wagon, the lid being nailed down after the last of the family had filed silently by, and the small coffin was placed in the shallow, dusty grave. White, talcum-colored earth was shoveled in the grave, sending up clouds of ashy dust. One of the men stepped forward, extending a handful of faded paper flowers taken off a neighboring mound of earth. He stuck them upright in the ground, one at a time.

". . . we commit the body of this child to the ground. . . ."

As the Bishop stepped back from the grave, a piercing scream went up from one of the women. The others joined in with mournful, throaty wails that rolled on and on over the silent, treeless plain. A man started singing:

Qu to kata ihan
Hed wanun kiciya ka pi ta. . . .
("We'll meet again in the sweet bye and bye. . . .")

The people returned to their wagons and jalopies.

"Which one is the mother?"

"Mother over in that wagon," pointed Chief Bartholomew. "She having new baby right now. Baptize maybe next week, elo?"

The Bishop prayed with the bereaved, expectant mother. Returning to his car, Alfred noted, "The wind is rising. It's turning colder. The air smells of snow, and it's eighty-three miles to St. Mary's for the Christ Mass at three in the afternoon. Dirt roads. Shortcut trails. Must start." He glanced at his watch. "It's now 1:20 P.M."

In the pass, a thousand feet above the valley the wind had risen to a fifty-mile-an-hour gale. The snow began, in horizontal strips like fuzzy string, racing across the windshield. Then: back down through the ridge for mile upon mile of hazy driving in the hypnotic dream of the man engulfed in enveloping whiteness of winter's storm; the sudden jarring as the car rides on to the shoulder of the road cuts short the delicious lulling of the whirling snow.

Back in Big Pine, there were seventy-five people jammed into the overheated little white church. One family had come fifty-three miles to make their Christmas Communion, and to have their infant son baptized. An old coffee pot was found and filled with snow, to be melted on the stove to provide water for the baptism. By the time the Creed had been said the pot was steaming. A solemn procession moved to the font, headed by a server wearing husking gloves and carrying the boiling water in the battered percolator. Clouds of steam enveloped the family and the procession as the water was poured into the cold stone font with a loud, coughing hiss.

"We receive this Child into the congregation of Christ's

59

flock; and do sign him with the sign of the Cross . . . (*wonder how that Indian woman came out?*)"

A Christmas sermon about cows. "How would you, with your knowledge, experiences, aptitudes, and abilities like to be compressed into the body of one of your steers and live with other cows who were not like that? This is what God did when He was born into the body of a child. 'Who for us men . . . came down. . . .' Mary, for whom this church was named, gave consent to be used as a means for God to enter human life."

And then, the Liturgy continued. "And to all thy People give thy heavenly grace; and especially to this congregation here present . . . (*in this cold, grey half-light of a Christmas Eve storm*) . . . Because thou didst give Jesus Christ . . . to be born as at this time for us . . . and . . . that we may continue in that holy fellowship. . . . The Peace of God, which passeth all understanding . . . remain with you always."

(*Is there time to take the short-cut to Gordon if one stalling is allowed? Let's go.*) The car had been filled to the roof with presents of food: roasts, steaks, chickens, bacon, eggs, canned vegetables, jams and preserves, a sack of potatoes, and Christmas cookies.

(*Mustn't forget. Go down back of the cattle-sales barn first.*) There, in a tent bulging out with the wind, sat an old squaw, squatting on a box with the family of ten gathering around her.

"Mr. Bishop here, Grandma. Bring Communion."

There was just time for a hamburger and a cup of coffee at the Daisy Cafe in Gordon before the evening Eucharist. The waitress picked up the check.

"Don't ask no questions because ain't supposed to say who paid. Now a piece of pie by me, Revener."

The sense of the nearness of our Lord's loving presence was strong among them all that night. More than half of those present had never witnessed the Lord's own service before. The congregation was silent—as in the stable nineteen hundred years ago.

> O holy child of Bethlehem!
>   Descend to us, we pray;
> Cast out our sin and enter in,
>   Be born in us to-day.

The wind had gone down. The snow fell in lazy flakes. The car picked up speed now, going down the highway. The flakes dashed themselves against the glass. An hour's silent ride back to the parish church in Bigview. Before the rich, golden curtain behind the altar hung a huge wreath of juniper boughs, the only decoration in the church except for the tall poinsettias on the altar, which was festively arrayed with the creamy white and gold covering made by a former priest, long since forgotten.

"O come, all ye faithful . . . (*the unfaithful are here, too, it looks like; I'll bet it has stopped snowing.*)" As in the stable of that first Christmas, here, too, were the ass of pride and the ox of prejudice, looking through unknowing eyes at all that was taking place—"But as many as received him, to them gave he power to become the sons of God. . . ."

On they came: the broken, the healed; the scarred from battle with sin; the young and new, fresh and glowing; the hopeful, the dulled, the eager, the joyous, the sad.

Two A.M. Fell into bed. Nothing to do until eight o'clock in the morning.

There came together on Christmas Day a handful of the faithful who could not be present at the midnight service. Once again "a great and mighty wonder today on earth is done." As the Bishop stood at the back of the church calling out greetings of "Merry Christmas," a young Indian boy waited patiently for the people to leave. "Hello, young man. Is

61

that a note for me?" asked Alfred as he saw the soiled envelope in the boy's hand.

He proffered it to the Bishop and waited. "Gotta wait for an answer."

A note penciled on a piece of gift wrapping said:

> Dear Mr. Father: Chrismas coming soon. Lots of Indians be on the town Concord. Big party at Little Wolfs. Many boys and girls not much toys. Shoes for bare feet. Clothes too need. How about come to camp on city dump on Concord on the night Chrismas. Bring altar. Vestments. Big book. 32 for communion. Bring voice. We sing carols waiting for S. Claus walking on the night please.
>
> PS, also shoes for old lady who wears rubbers only now and dry pants for baby babtise. Inform boy. thank you.
>
> Joe Sits Holy

Alfred took the young lad with him to the hotel cafe for lunch and then made a date to meet him there at four in the afternoon so he could ride home with the Bishop. In the meantime Alfred went scavenging for clothes and contacted the Dooperway manager, who came to the store and gave Alfred all perishable foods and candy, some cigarettes and cigars. "This will save Leo Bent-in-the-Head from trying to swipe a cigar," explained Vern, the manager. The Bishop thanked him, and went on his way.

In the gathering darkness of the late Christmas afternoon, Alfred and the boy set off for a forty-seven-mile ride over icy roads, the car packed tight with gifts and requested items, and portable altar. There, in a shack with a ceiling barely tall enough to stand erect, and not much larger than the Bishop's living room, were gathered fifty-one Indians. Seated on planks supported by empty oil drums the congregation silently (and confidently) awaited the beginning of the evening festivities.

Facing the east wall, and under the only window in the

hovel, the altar was set up on a rickety table alongside the community Christmas tree. Popcorn chains of indeterminate age supplemented the pieces of broken colored glass, fashioned in odd design by bubble gum, and the faded wrappings which served as ornaments.

Standing before the people, Alfred put on his cassock,

Seated on planks supported by empty oil drums the congregation silently awaited the beginning of the evening festivities.

surplice, and a white, beaded stole made many years ago by a Sioux squaw. It was a profound and humbling experience to celebrate a feast of the Holy Nativity in a shack on the city dump amidst the cast off and the rejected, having only the light of two candles flickering in the overheated darkness.

He moved the sleeping dog gently with his foot to a safer place under the altar, and removed a battle-scarred tomcat from the lower branches of the Christmas tree. As he turned to hand the cat to Joe, Alfred nearly fell over the squatted figure of a ninety-year-old blind squaw directly beside the altar already holding out her hands to receive her communion.

The Holy Mysteries began . . . "There was no room for Him at the inn . . . (*O God, what has the white man done, charging into their stone-age culture as we have? Our Lord and His Church are here atoning for the sins of His children against these simple people* . . .) . . . Take . . . eat . . . in remembrance that Christ died for thee . . . feed on him in thy heart . . . (*Nineteen hundred years ago He came to earth, born in an outbuilding on the edge of town. He comes again tonight to a city dump, the dwelling place of the outcast. He must feel right at home.*). . . ."

The Sacrament was received first by the men, then the young mothers, holding out one hand while clutching their nursing infants with the other.

(*Some of them are without husbands, or even a man to bring them bread. Some of the children are white. That baby sleeping in its mother's arms can't be more than two or three days old.*) Finally the older children and the old squaws received, all silently seated and pressed together.

As the Bishop began to replace the sacred vessels on the altar the chief stepped forward and, apologizing to him for speaking in Dacotah, addressed the gathering. Alfred was called upon to make a speech. (*He performed badly, he thought.*) The Chief then told the Christmas story in their language first, repeating it in English for the younger ones.

"Santa is coming," he announced, "he is just now passing through Bigview and walking fast. Wife right behind. Only forty miles to go. We wait for him and sing carols real loud so he find us in the dark. Make him hear noise."

They sang carols and praised God in Dacotah and English for nearly an hour. Finally, there was a loud knocking on the door. In strode a huge Santa dressed in a moth-eaten raccoon coat with a white scarf tied around his neck and a weather-beaten mask pinned to the front of the visor on a railroader's cap. He was greeted with much laughter and many taunting remarks.

"Why so late, old man?" "You walk from North Pole, old Camp Robber?" "What's in the sack? Old crow" "Dead jack-rabbit?" "Where did you steal the presents?"

For nearly two hours the slow, steady distribution of gifts went on. One orange at a time, one piece of candy at a time, wrapped gifts one at a time. There were pocket combs and hand lotion for everyone. There were dolls for every girl child and toy autos for every boy. There were comic books for everyone. The Bishop was presented with a beaded leather purse the size of a money bag. Finally Santa was presented with a lighted Christmas candle and forcibly escorted to the door with the words, "Good night old man. This candle help you find your way like the star help the Wise Men and Jesus help us."

Alfred was starting slowly toward the door when Joe spoke. "There's a baby to baptize yet."

"Oh, yes; which one now?" asked the weary father-in-God.

"The one born yesterday by the mother in the wagon. You bury her other one. She want to name him for you. Okay? Elo."

VII

Crisis at Grace Church

THE BILLBOARDS, now increasing in numbers, informed the Bishop of Blunderland that he was approaching the metropolis of Ardmore, still five miles away, but visible under a pall of industrial smoke that was draped over the older part of the city along the river. He passed first through Ardmore Estates, a sprawling, smog-hazed future slum made up of housing developments of a stupefying sameness and insanity-producing standardization with curly-cued lanes having pseudo-romantic and status-creating names—very sophisticated. Alfred noted that in each mortgaged driveway there was a mortgaged car standing beside a mortgaged house, and each mortgaged "homeowner" was indulging in graceful and casual suburban living by following a mortgaged power-mower around the yard while wearing his new charge-account Bermuda shorts. Block after block of these country-estates, lived in by America's thirty-day tycoons, surrounded Ardmore as a kind of cultural moat around the Victorian castles of the inner city.

"But their credit is good," observed Alfred.

Fifteen minutes later Chatworthy pulled his car up at the curb in front of fashionable Grace Protestant Episcopal Church, the Reverend E. Sewickley Codger, D.D., Rector. Today a class of confirmands would be presented by Dr. Codger to the Bishop for the Laying-on-of-Hands. Mrs. Griselda Galsworthy III had instructed her chauffeur to carry the Bishop's vestment case to the sacristy, and sure enough, here he came around the walk, complete with puttees and gloves to assist his lordship.

The Bishop waved to the Gripinghams, who had just parked across the street, and made his way to the Parish House. He was greeted by the Reverend Roderick Primtoe, the curate, and was escorted to the sacristy to put on his vestments. As he picked his way through a swarm of veiled and white-dressed girl confirmands, he observed the usual polite Sunday scuffle of eighth-and ninth-grade boy confirmands, pushing and shoving each other self-consciously as they awaited the processional countdown.

"Good morning, Alfred," cordially greeted Dr. Codger. "I see that you have been properly taken care of while I was busy with the choir." Sewickley watched the Bishop curiously as he withdrew a cope and mitre from the vestment case. "Isn't that thing something new?" he asked cautiously.

"Just received it last week as a gift from my boyhood parish. Lovely material, isn't it?" replied Alfred, a little nervously. He wasn't sure whether Codger knew what a cope was, but he did beat him to an opinion. "This is to be used strictly for Confirmations, Sewickley, so don't suspect that I am trying to introduce the Swahili Rite here at Grace Church."

"Well-l-l, it's never been our custom here, you know. The people like the plain and simple worship," stalled Codger, trying to get up enough courage to take a definite stand against such medieval restorations.

"Like Mrs. Galsworthy's new hat or the Gripingham's Belchfire convertible, perhaps," taunted Alfred with a slightly wicked smile. "Relax, Codger," he went on. "By the time that I have explained the reasonableness of a cope we shall have all the Vestry wanting one for you."

"If I received one of those—er—things, I'd have it made into a frontal, which is where it belongs in the first place," objected the Rector.

"Come to think of it, Sewickley," Alfred replied, as he put

on the mitre, "it could be remade into a nice, gay pall. Just the thing to put over a Bishop's casket, too." The Bishop glanced at his watch and conversationally cut in front of Codger. "Three minutes to eleven. Time to get in the order of march." Codger always zigged when Chatworthy zagged and never seemed able to reverse his field in time to take the offensive.

As the procession started down the aisle and the Bishop emerged from the cloister which connected the church to the Parish Hall, he beheld a crowded nave on either side of the large choir, which was marching in a heavy sway to "Fling out the Banner, high and wide." "And the banners are flung out, too," Alfred observed, "All eight flags following the crucifer." As the Bishop entered the sanctuary, the flags dipping and swaying in a line outside the altar rail, the Church Flag whipped his mitre, but not quite hard enough to knock it off. "The Rector will take that as poetic justice if the Church Flag knocks off my hat," he thought, smiling. "I feel like I'm being enveloped in bunting. This must be what it's like to be buried at sea." He proceeded to the Bishop's chair and succeeded in knocking over the taper which had been propped up against his prayer desk.

Like the look-out in a ship's crow's nest, he looked out over the congregation, and, during the last verse of the hymn, watched the Confirmation class being marshalled together in preparation for the Laying-on-of-Hands. He felt as though he was being lowered with ropes into his childhood. On the last breath of the Amen the Bishop strode quickly to the chancel step and motioned for everyone to be seated. The congregation was half-way seated anyway, but the unusual action of the Bishop caught everyone in mid-air. The Rector was left stranded in the middle of the aisle, zigging again to the Bishop's zag. Codger squeezed into the fourth pew on the gospel side in a state of confusion, as though he were the victim of the hidden ball play.

"Brethren," began the Bishop, "on such a glorious occasion as this day it seems fitting and proper for us to receive these boys and girls into the full life of the Church with all gravity and seriousness. Personally, I have always disliked having the Confirmation class line up at the altar rail and then administering the Laying-on-of-Hands by passing down the row. This always seems to me to be too much of an assembly line, especially at a time when our children are being set aside in a special kind of ordination as consecrated laymen and laywomen. Why, even in our public schools, when a graduate receives his diploma, it is done individually. Of course, this rite marks the beginning of their knowledge which shall, God willing, continue without interruption. . . ."

Johnny Smithwick turned to Donald Davis, a fellowconfirmand and whispered, "Does he mean we hafta keep going to Sunday School?"

"Naw, that's just the Bishop talking," retorted Donald. The Bishop observed the conversational exchange.

"So, this morning," he continued, "I propose that I be seated here at the chancel step and have each child come forward to receive the Laying-on-of-Hands individually. I do not believe that this will cause undue confusion."

Dr. Codger controlled himself well, which was more than he could do for the situation, considering that he was a person who saw to it that every maneuver was executed according to plan, and then along comes this Bishop and throws everything into chaos.

"Many of you, doubtless, are wondering what these vestments are that I am wearing today," Alfred went on smoothly. "They were given to me by my boyhood parish, and just received last week. I am happy that my first opportunity to wear the cope and mitre coincided with my visit to Grace Church." Not a bit of butter was melting in his mouth, but Alfred perceived that the congregation was softening up, except for Dr.

Codger who was thinking dark thoughts about the episcopate.

"Brethren, a 'cope' is simply a Latin word for 'cape.' It is made of quite heavy material. This reminds the Bishop that he wears the sins of his people and bears their weight." Alfred paused for it to sink in. "The scarlet reminds us of the nature of our sins as well as of the martyrs, who stuck by their guns and lost their life blood because of their love of their Lord. The gold stands for our offering to the Lord Jesus of our means and our lives, both of which are precious to us. This recalls that practicing the Christian religion is expensive. If it isn't worth anything, then it can't be much good, can it?" Alfred noted that he had the attention of everyone. "And the mitre," he said as he removed it, "is a sign of the tongues of fire that descended upon the Apostles at Pentecost, or Whitsunday."

With those words he announced the hymn. While everyone, including Dr. Codger, was collecting himself after this most irregular interruption, Alfred requisitioned a folding chair from an acolyte and seated himself in the center of the aisle and, one by one, the candidates came forward and knelt before the Bishop.

"Defend, O Lord, this thy Child with thy heavenly grace; that he may continue thine for ever; and daily increase in thy Holy Spirit more and more, until he come unto thy everlasting kingdom. . . ."

As Johnny Smithwick approached, Alfred quickly breathed a prayer that this young lad might receive the gift of wisdom (this being a secret and pious custom of certain bishops). Johnny was quite serious about the whole thing, but when his friend Donald came up swaggering and grinning, at his turn, Alfred planned to stop that quickly. Donald knelt and bowed his head so low that the Bishop could barely touch him. Chatworthy leaned far over and placed his hands over the boy's ears, pinched the lobes and forced him erect. Laying hands on

"Naw, that's just the Bishop talking."

him was heavily done with the episcopal ring deliberately cracking Donald sharply, and he pushed the sign of the cross into his forehead with his thumb. Donald returned to his seat subdued.

Forty-two children later, the choir and congregation joined together and sang "O Jesus I have promised to serve Thee to the end." As Alfred returned to the sanctuary and the Bishop's chair, he noted the complete absence of adults in the class. "It's still a children's rite here at Grace Church," he observed.

At the end of the hymn, the Bishop stepped into the pulpit and waited for everyone to be comfortably settled—a weekly performance of ancient usage. "A people that yawns is ready for revolt," he thought. He folded his notes, descended from the pulpit, and stood in the aisle at the chancel steps and began to preach.

The congregation received another shock as the Bishop spoke directly to the Confirmation class. "Since all members of the class are growing young men and women, I think it only right that I should address my remarks today especially to them. Of course, the others may listen, but it is to them that I am primarily speaking." He paused and smiled.

Concealing her lips with the Sunday bulletin now rendered useless, Mrs. E. Charles Cheadle whispered to her pew mate, "The Bishop is actually ignoring us. He isn't acting like a bishop at all."

"He's too frank to suit me," replied Miss Rimplesash. "It isn't right for a Bishop to be like that."

Alfred was saying, "When I was a boy I lived in a small town in the Midwest, and our house was right on the bank of a big river. Some of us boys had a shack over on the island. I spent all summer over there. Oh," he hastened to add, "I always came home to eat, as we all did, but we truly had a Tom Sawyer boyhood on that river.

"Well, one day, as I was going to the island alone in my

rowboat, I pulled the old scow up on the mud bank and started up the path to our shack. There on the path ahead of me, about as far away as the length of this aisle, there was a crow sittting on the ground. Now, if you know anything about crows, you know that they usually go around in committees of five or six. However, crows have committees that get things done. Every day they appoint one of the committee to be look-out chairman, and he sits all day in the top of a tree to give warning while the other crows feed on the ground. Today, this crow was alone. That meant that he had been deserted, for some reason. I soon found out what that was, for as soon as I started walking toward him he tried to fly away and he could barely get off the ground. When I got closer I saw that there was a clam fastened on to one of his claws."

Chatworthy even had the attention of the ushers at this point. He continued. "This crow had been fishing down along the mud bank and had stepped on this clam and the clam had been with him ever since. The crow went down to the mud flats often enough to keep the clam wet, so the clam was well and happy, and stayed right where he was. Of course, what was happening was that the clam was slowly killing that crow. Already I could see that the crow was growing weaker, and probably didn't have many more days to live. You see, that clam was keeping that crow from being the kind of a creature that God meant him to be. Well, boys and girls, I ran up to that crow, threw my jacket over him, and took my knife and pried the clam off the crow's foot and let him fly away. I had been the means that God used to give that crow's life back to him so that he could be the kind of creature that God had in mind for him in the first place."

"What is he driving at?" whispered Mrs. Woodburn.

"Keep on listening, Eva," replied her husband, "it's the first sensible discourse that I've heard in this church for a long time."

"Now," continued Alfred, getting ready to close in for the

kill, "each one of you has something wrong with you. So do your parents. So do I. It's called a besetting sin, which means that there is something about each one of us that keeps us from becoming the kind of person that God has in mind for us to be. It's sort of like the clam on the crow's foot. If you don't get rid of it, then it will get rid of you. Baptism and Confirmation are the Church's way of taking the clam off your foot so that you can become what God wants you to be. Making your communions faithfully and regularly is the Church's way of helping to keep from getting another clam on your foot."

Chatworthy noticed an uncomfortable shift to alternate hams among the faithful. He decided to press for discomfort. "Then there are many ways of keeping the clam off. Sacramentally, there are Holy Communion, which I have already mentioned, and Holy Unction, or anointing with oil. Just remember, that, if, in spite of everything, you get another clam back on your spiritual foot, then confession of sins and forgiveness gets rid of it again and again. Well," the Bishop added, "that's another instruction. I think that we had better finish this one first."

The congregation settled back, upon hearing the good news, and, faintly hoping that the Bishop had provided enough raw meat for the day and would now lapse into some convenient and conservative pieties, prepared for the frosting of the comfortable gospel. They expected him to gloss over what had so far been a disturbing morning and give blessed assurance to the faithful at Grace Church that they were doing all right, and with the Lord's blessing, too.

Alas! It was not so to be. The Bishop merely continued the alarming and unconventional strain. "This morning, when your Bishop laid hands on you he simply did what our Lord did to His friends. They thought that it was important enough to continue the practice, so everyone who joined with them in the holy fellowship also received the Laying-on-of-Hands from them. That has continued right down through the years, including this morning. Everyone who has received the Laying-on-of-Hands in this manner is related to our Lord by touch. If everyone through all the ages could join hands, then there would be an unbroken line from our Lord Himself right down to this step and to you."

Codger cogitated. Griselda Galsworthy III thought and approved. So far, so good. "Do you remember that I pressed my thumb into this oil stock? There is cotton in there into which was poured olive oil, which was blessed last Maundy Thursday, the night that Jesus was arrested in the Garden. Then I made the sign of the cross on your forehead. There's nothing magic about that, boys and girls. Now back in Jesus' day, in that hot, dry climate, your skin would become dry and crack, and you couldn't breathe through your skin. Every one of you know that you breathe through our skin and your nose, too. So, after you had done a day's work and had come home and taken a bath, you would take olive oil and rub it into your skin. That would open up the pores and soften up your skin, and you had another way to breathe! This is simply the Church's way of showing you, that, now that you have taken on additional responsibilities, God will give you an extra strength. An extra way to breathe, so to speak."

The congregation perceptibly sighed as Alfred gazed upon the intent faces of young America in the first four rows.

"Let's see, what did I do next?" he went on. "Oh, yes, then I pressed my ring on your forehead. The Bishop's ring has the seal, or the brand, of the Diocese carved on it. I branded you with the mark of our Lord's ranch, the Diocese of Blunderland, so now he'll know you spiritually when He sees you!" A smiling approval was barely discernible as the relieved congregation knew most certainly that the Bishop was just talking to children.

"That's kind of sweet," thought the Reverend Mr. Primtoe's mother.

"There's some more coming," pursued Alfred. "Remember? I tapped each of you on the cheek! That is the Church's way, through her bishops, to tell you to wake up!" Alfred clapped his hands together and everyone shifted. "Now, look, boys and girls, tomorrow you go back to school and you are going to find just as many difficult things to deal with as you did last week. You are also going to find just as many impossible people to put up with as there were last week. Only now there can be a difference. Now, and perhaps for the first time, you can begin to see people and things through our Lord's eyes. When you do, then the things that you have to do won't seem nearly as difficult, and the people that you have to put up with won't be as impossible. Each of us sees man's world through our plain eyes. We see God's world through our Lord's eyes, and it's a lot nicer place, believe me."

The Bishop beckoned to the curate. "Reverend Sir, may I borrow your hand for a moment? Come along with it if you wish." This was greeted by laughter from the children and disapproving frowns of the archaic Church.

"I shall greet Mr. Primtoe in the American manner," announced the Bishop. "We each extend the right hand of friendship. But does either of us surrender much? For all I know, Mr. Primtoe may be left handed and I would be at a disadvantage. Or, for all he knows, I may have knowledge of judo." More laughter and more disapproval. "Now, boys and girls, I shall greet him as Jesus greeted his friends like this." Alfred placed his hands on Primtoe's shoulders and bent his own body forward in the embrace known as the Kiss of Peace. "See how defenceless I am? I cannot even see what he might be up to. This is the Church's way of saying that you are now welcomed into this defenceless fellowship."

Chatworthy thanked Mr. Primtoe, who tripped over the kneeler and returned to his seat, amidst suppressed giggling. The Bishop was obviously being carried away. He descended the chancel step and stood directly in the aisle and asked the class if they remembered the story of the Prodigal Son. Alfred knew better than to press the matter by asking for a raising of hands, so he plunged right in. "It was the story of a young man who asked for his part of the family money and his dad gave it to him. He went to the big city and lived pretty high, party after party, until all his money was gone. He tried to get a job, but there was a depression on, and all he could get to do was to help feed the pigs for the city scavenger service. One day he was so hungry that he climbed into the pen and fought with the pigs for food. Then and there he decided to go home and ask his father to forgive him. All this time the father had not heard from him. He hadn't written any letters home. He hadn't sent any telegrams. He had not even called long distance, collect. His father had no way of knowing what life away from home had done to him. Then one day, as the father was looking out the doorway he saw his son coming up the road. His clothes were in rags, he walked with a limp, and it appeared that he was sick. Still, the father didn't know if he was play-acting or not. He didn't know if the son was coming home to ask forgiveness, ask for more money, burn down the barn, or whether he was planning on killing everybody there and take it all. But even so, the father ran down the road and greeted his son as I just greeted each one of you when you knelt on this step. 'Welcome home and no questions asked.'

"So, there we are!" concluded Alfred, "welcomed into this defenseless fellowship, with our eyes opened, marked with the Lord's brand, given another way to breathe, and now related to our Blessed Lord by touch. And besides that, we got the clam off your foot. We really got a lot done today, didn't we?—and now may our Blessed Lord always give you a loving sense of His near Presence. Amen."

Later that afternoon, as Alfred was driving over to St. Lethargus', Sunken Heights, to institute the new rector, he reflected on the day's work thus far. "Their necks are so stiff from watching the sky and waiting for it to open that I don't think they would know if it did," he mused. "I wish that Codger would get them out of the alcove into the outer court of the temple, and then come in with them. They are all members of the Church Reluctant." He heard the familiar whining scream of the patrol car siren and habitually pulled to the shoulder of the highway and waited.

"Good afternoon, Noah, are you on every beat in this state?"

VIII

The Bishop and the Bobbsey Twins at Camp

"PRAY AND PLAY AT CAMP WOB-A-LEE ON WILD-FISH LAKE," happily announced the folder prepared by the Division of Camps and Conferences of the Diocese of Blunderland. "Nestled amid the hills in Paradise Valley we camp under the tall whispering pines in the fragrance of pine-scented western air and sleep under the stars. Camp Wob-A-Lee is the ideal spot for worship and recreation."

"And so it is," agreed the Bishop, although he felt that the description was a little overdone, probably because it was written during Lent by a priest living on the high plains. "However, things that can't happen anywhere else *do* happen at camp. I had better plan on being there for the opening day, and for the closing, too." He recalled painfully that the lavatories had not been properly drained last year, and the error had compounded to an additional expense of four hundred dollars.

Nevertheless, Alfred genuinely looked forward to this part of his episcopal duty. He was quite happy in the following days making his own private preparations to sleep under the stars and the whispering pines by getting a new sleeping bag to replace the one missing from last year. He put cold patches on the air mattress where it had been torn while being hoisted over a barbed wire fence into Tompkins pasture by the occupants of St. Alban's cabin tent on the last night of camp. New jeans and a new sweatshirt, plus fresh flashlight batteries, were added to his pack as he eagerly awaited the day. Due to his unusual capacity to idealize the past, Alfred had projected great dreams for what was to be accomplished while he was there—in terms of capital improvements—by dint of his hammer and saw.

Kathleen noted the symptoms, and privately diagnosed that her husband was going into what she mournfully called one of his "nesting periods." She knew by experience that nothing would be safe. Thus, she stayed out of his way and arranged to have a full calendar which would make it impossible for her to accompany the Bishop on the great adventure. A wise woman, indeed.

Alfred decided to go to camp two days before the season was to begin. Although he was aware that impatience dries the blood sooner than sorrow or old age, still, he could not fight the urge to tackle the wilderness of Camp Wob-A-Lee. Besides, next Sunday was free from engagements.

"Farewell, Kathleen. I'm about to take off in a cloud of old hymnals," he cheerily called out, when the Eocene 6 was loaded for the two hundred-mile trip.

"Now, Alfred, for heaven's sake, hold the hammer with both hands this year, will you? And don't chop down trees when there are any cars around. I was never so embarrassed in my life as that time you felled a tree across the Lautzenheiser's new Buick—and Gramps Lautzenheiser in the back seat. Remember you're the Bishop, not Paul Bunyan."

"It didn't even wake the old man up," recalled the apostle of the wilderness. "But out of my deep concern for your peace of mind, I shall exercise the utmost caution in carrying out my plans and hack down only the trees that have bears in them."

"I don't take in a word of it," said Kathleen as she bade Alfred goodby, good camping, and good chopping.

After a two-hour drive Alfred reached the point of no return and pulled off to the side of the road in front of the Horse Creek Lodge for a hamburger and a cup of coffee. As he seated himself at the counter, he noticed a new sign back of the cash register in this tired old short-order house, "One more crack like that and out you go." The numerous other signs had the old sameness. He finished his repast in silence, attempting to overcome the sullen resistance to mastication of an antique piece of apple pie, and then called for his check.

"Bishop, the man that just went out the door paid for it," explained the waitress.

"What did he do that for? I don't know him."

"He said for me to tell you to say a little prayer for him."

"Another professional Irishman, I'll bet," suspected Alfred. "I am never safe from being a kept man in public places with characters like that lurking around every counter."

The Bishop did have the presence of mind to thank the waitress and to slip a dime under his plate, convinced that his benefactor wouldn't leave an allegedly non-praying waitress anything. As he walked to his car he saw his florid-faced host with a cigar sticking out of his face like a tent peg, waving to him as he roared up the highway in a Belchfire 8.

"Just as I thought," he muttered to himself. "Thinks he's on the inside track with his two-bit charities. He'd better start rattling his own beads." He drove off with a rumble and jerk, in the Eocene 6, and charged onward into the late afternoon and Camp Wob-A-Lee where "we pray and play together in the Alps of America."

It was strangely quiet around the camp as the Bishop arrived. He discovered immediately that it was closed tight, still winterized, and everything under lock and key. Not even a new tire mark in front of the lodge. "Now where in thunder is Cudlipp? He was supposed to have everything in readiness."

What the Bishop was slowly discovering was that although

the Reverend Gregory Cudlipp was a former professional camping director, prior to entering Federal Seminary, he had been brain-washed by the Pastoral Theology professor into accepting the "big lie" ("Now, gentlemen, when you have done your stint in the mission field and get your parish in the East, etc."). Cudlipp was now on the first step of the ladder of success, content to make his mistakes here while patiently waiting for the eastern dream to materialize. It all annoyed the Bishop, for he prided himself on his ability to cull such men from his prospects for work in the Diocese.

With his anger rising by the second, he got back in the car and drove furiously to town. By the time he arrived there, he had calmed down somewhat, only to find the vicarage locked and the steps a clutter of newspapers. Brooding dark thoughts, Alfred drove directly to the Stockmen's Bar on Main Street, not to drown his troubles, but to find some hired hands, shaky as they might be, to help him in his hour of trial, and assist in getting Camp Wob-A-Lee ready for praying and playing.

Every bottle and glass came down on the bar in a chorus of exclamation and surprise as the Bishop crossed the threshold where old friends meet. Going directly to the bartender to enlist his aid in conscripting some labor, he heard an old man at the end of the counter announce for all to hear, "I been comin' in saloons all my life. First the women come in and now a preacher. It's too much. I'm gittin' out."

Alfred and the bartender smiled at the philosophical complaint and concluded their business. The Bishop found two helpers, including one who recommended himself as an expert in lock-picking. It would save chopping the hasps off, which might have given Alfred some small satisfaction for his frustration and anger.

Two days later, three tired men had finished preparing the Camp, and still Cudlipp had not appeared. The Bishop secretly hoped by then that he had exchanged his little grey home in the West for a little green grave in the East. The entire enterprise ended satisfactorily, and Alfred drove the men back to town where they enjoyed a steak dinner. The helpers were paid off and thanked. A handshake all around and Chatworthy returned to Camp to await the arrival of the campers.

Upon his return he saw that some of them had already arrived, the scene quickly taking on the characteristic confusion of opening day, with campers and parents arriving before the staff. Right behind him, however, came Father Hammerchest, the Dean of the first period. The Bishop suppressed his grimness and showed himself to be genuinely happy at the gathering of his children.

As the day wore on, and more and more arrived and the excitement grew, Alfred found that something else had gone wrong. He watched Alaric Donebetter drive up with a car full of teenagers and another carload behind, both from Flathead City. "This camp period is for the fourth-fifth- and sixth-graders," Alfred recalled. "What is Alaric doing with ten high school youth here?"

At the registration desk, Miss Myrtle Mossbottom, who was taking in cash and assigning the tents and cots, discovered that Donebetter, in the interests of economy, had used last year's registration blanks, moving the dates up one day by a ball point pen correction. He had not stopped to remember that the high school camp was to be at the end of the camping season. There was nothing to do but let them stay, even though it meant going back to town for two more tents. As Alfred walked back to the trench that he was digging outside the kitchen, he had several uncharitable thoughts about Alaric Donebetter.

Alfred had the feeling that he was being watched as he dug in the clay trench. By now he had struck water and was sloshing around in the mess when he looked up through the blear of perspiration in answer to a question posed by the suspected ditch superintendent.

"Hey, bud, 'ya seen the old man around? Somebody said he came out this way."

"Old man?" queried the battle-scarred denizen of the ditch, knowing full well that it was he that the questioner was seeking.

"The Bishop. I think the old boy saw me up in the lodge and headed for the hills," explained the man, as he leaned over and spat in the trench.

"Oh, yeah. Let's see. I seen him go down to the lower camp," Alfred answered, vulgarizing his voice and attempting to suppress a satanic leer. "Follow that there path down across the road about a half a mile and then go up into the timber." He went back to his digging, averting his face, as the man and his angular wife turned without a "thank you" and began to follow his directions.

"I hope Grandpa Kopek sees him and chases him off his property with a shotgun. Old man, am I?" The mud flew out of the trench in great clods.

Several hours later, the strains of "Now the day is over" drifted out across the lake as the dying embers of the campfire flickered a feeble light to guide the campers to their cabins. Eventually the excitement died down and within the hour the staff gathered in the kitchen for the meeting of organization. The Reverend Gregory Cudlipp had arrived, but having been advised of the Bishop's frame of mind, had managed so far to avoid him. The eastern seaboard's gift to the Rocky Mountain diocese had explained, not without pain, that he had climbed Mt. Cliffhang and had been rimrocked for eighteen hours. When Alfred heard of it he opined that it wasn't nearly long enough, but dismissed the matter as something that only the Cudlipps of this world could possibly get involved in.

Father Hammerchest opened the meeting by passing out

typed copies of the daily schedule. "You will note, ladies and gentlemen, that I have advanced the rising hour to six A.M. The campers will be allowed ten minutes to present themselves for thirty minutes of setting-up exercises. This will be followed every day by a run around the lake and then breakfast at eight o'clock . . ."

"But, Chesty," interrupted the Reverend Phineas Holihill, "there has been no time set aside for morning devotions. Now I have here," he added, as he presented his version of the schedule, "Morning Prayer at six A.M., followed by a thirty minute period of mental prayer, and a solemn celebration of the Eucharist at seven. We can certainly be ready for breakfast by eight o'clock, except on Thursday. That's St. Hubert's Day, patron saint of the woods," he explained, "when I plan on a Solemn High Mass followed by a procession and Benediction."

The Bishop was about to straighten Father Holihill out on the matter of unauthorized services—not taken from the Prayer Book—when a scream went up from the inner fastness of the walk-in cooler, followed instantly by the appearance of the cook, her eyes fairly bugging out of her head as she weakly shouted, "Snakes!" and pointed wildly behind her.

The Reverend Mr. Herpey, who up till now had taken an indifferent attitude toward the rising debate, rushed into the cooler and retrieved his gunny sack of snakes. He excused himself for his forgetfulness, apologized to the cook, and opened the bag for a quick inspection. Holding up a limp handful of chilled snakes Mr. Herpey explained that he wanted only to hibernate them because his wife refused to stay home with a houseful of reptiles while he was at camp. The cook lurched off in the general direction of her quarters with threats dwindling into the distance of what would happen if Herpey ever set foot in that kitchen again. He honestly could not understand her violent reaction.

"*I did so much want to use my pets in my lectures this week or original sin.*"

"I did so much want to use my pets in my lectures this week on original sin according to the Post-Nicene Fathers," he lamented.

"Herpey," interrupted the Bishop, "please keep those blasted snakes in your tent, and *keep track of them.* The children may watch you feed them only if they wish, and then it must be at a remote spot. We'll have no more reptile panics, or frightening cooks or children at camp. Interesting as it might be, there will not be any snakes at classes or we will all witness an example of original sin at its worst as I remove you and your pets from the scene." He paused. "Sorry, Paul, but that's that. Nothing personal."

The staff barely believed it, but were about to resume the debate when the Bishop took advantage of the break to move in. "Now, let's see, Charles," he said, speaking to Fr. Hammerchest, who was still staring, jut-jawed, at Phineas Holihill, "you are scheduled to give a course on the Athletes of God, I believe."

"That's right, Bishop," hastily agreed Chesty. "Starting right off tomorrow with St. Christopher, the greatest weight-lifter of them all." He twitched a bicep and smiled a knowing grin. "Then on to St. John Bosco who invented the polevault. Then the second-century cave hermits of the upper Nile and their dietary habits. It's all worked out," he concluded confidently.

"I see," said the Bishop as he massaged his aching forearm, stiff from two days labor in the pits. "And now, Phineas, what are your teaching plans?" he said, turning to the Chaplain.

"The Prayer Book of Edward the Sixth, 1549, your Lordship," piously replied Fr. Holihill. He filled in the ensuing stunned silence by commenting that he was confident that everyone at camp wanted the Church to carry on just as though the Reformation had never happened.

"There may be a difference of opinion in certain circles,

Phineas. But let us press on and adjust these matters in a moment."

"That unreconstructed medievalist really believes that any age gone by was better," he mused; then he addressed the Reverend Mr. Piper: "Peter, you are going to take charge of recreation and campfires, I presume?"

"Indeed so, sir. I apologize for not arriving in time to conduct the opening program, but all that will be rectified tomorrow. I have several games planned which will get everyone acquainted." Then Piper brightly added, "I have composed new words to 'Let Me Call You Sweetheart' which has some sound teaching content." Without delay he broke into the chorus:

> Please don't call me Charlie,
>   I'm not your neighbor any more.
> You may call me "Father"
>   Though a term that I deplore.
> I'd like to be called "Padre"
>   A word I recommend.
> You may call me anything,
>   But don't call me "Reverend."

"Now, I have several songs all well worked out which I'm sure will add fun to our campfires."

Again, deathly silence from all and poisonous stares between Fathers Hammerchest and Holihill.

"As you all know," the Bishop continued desperately, "Miss Myrtle Mossbottom, physical education director at Hungry Horse High School, has consented to be our waterfront director and conduct handicraft. We appreciate having you take of your summer holiday to be with us through the camp season, Myrtle. We just couldn't do better." The Bishop beamed.

Myrtle beamed right back, and then added, "And, Bishop, I have a new handicraft activity to institute anywhere for the first time. You see, I am going to be kept busy giving swimming instruction and life guarding, so I plan to teach handicraft down on the dock by giving instruction in basket weaving under water."

The Bishop, feeling completely checkmated, went slowly to the stove for a cup of strong coffee, wishing with all his heart that the Chairman of the Department of Camps and Conferences, who had assigned the staff, was within stoning distance. He returned to his place at the head of the table and stalled for one more brief instant with the desperate hope that the heavens would open, and amid the sounding of trumpets, lay in his hand, on a golden scroll, the schedule for the coming week. He lifted his eyes unto the hills, took a breath, and started in.

"Ladies and gentlemen, we seem to have a conflict of opinion and purpose regarding the camping experience here at Wob-A-Lee. I have, er . . . a . . . anticipated this, and have prepared a program which combines the merits and values of each person who will be contributing to the education of our boys and girls."

Hammerchest looked wary, but said nothing. Alfred continued.

"There will be a daily celebration of the Holy Communion, with vestments, but a minimum of ceremonial, a Field-Mass, so to speak," he added brightly, "for this is quite suitable to our surroundings. Charles will lead off after breakfast with his course on the Athletes of God. He may enlist any candidates for body building and meet with them daily at any time that does not conflict with classwork." He was relieved to see that Hammerchest thought that he had come off pretty well, judging by his triumphant expression as he gazed calmly at Phineas Holihill. The Bishop was quick to pick this up and hastened to assure Fr. Holihill that Evensong and Compline would be said daily.

"Holihill thinks I'm a black protestant, anyway," Alfred

consoled himself. Addressing himself to Herpey, he suggested, "The doctrine of the Creeds is just the thing to teach our boys and girls, so I'd like to have you take that over, Herpey. And you, Cudlipp, if you can stay off rock ledges for the week, will teach them how to find their way through the Prayer Book. Also I might add, go over Psalm 119, by yourself, a few times this week—especially that part about 'wherewithal shall a young man cleanse his way'—and then we will all feel better."

"Thank you, Bishop," quietly answered a subdued Cudlipp. "Does Absolution go with that penance?"

The Bishop placed his hand on his shoulder. "Greg, you got rimrocked, and that's the story of your life. As for me, I'm always getting in hot water, and that's my story. Let's forget it."

Everyone relaxed from the tension that Alfred had, one way or another, brought into the meeting. He bade them all goodnight, left them to hold a postmortem, and set off for his tent—and to spend the next thirty minutes trying to find his bedroll in the dark. As usual he discovered it in Tompkins pasture.

"I wonder what the Bishop of Fanfare is doing tonight? I'll bet that he didn't have to look for his bed."

IX

Popes, Plots, and Parishes

THE BISHOP of Blunderland informed his wife that he would walk to work this midsummer morning. "After two weeks at that Bishops' Group Life Laboratory, I am suffering a bad case of bookkeeper's beam. I need exercise regularly and purpose so to do," he said firmly.

"Call me when you want a ride home," answered his wife, knowing the brevity of his resolutions. "You are facing two weeks' mail and several phone messages which Miss Platen stalled on. She said something about arranging a luncheon meeting with a committee from St. Mitre's, Sedalia."

As the Bishop, still walking briskly and full of high resolve, strode past the Motor Harbor Filling Station, he was hailed by Ovid O'Shaughnessy, "Good morning, your excellency. We got the hose fastened back on the gas pump that you pulled off when the faucet was left in the tank. Hadn't seen you around. Thought maybe you was afraid to come back."

"Not at all, not at all," boomed the Bishop. "I have been away getting grouped."

"Is that anything like having an audience with the Pope?"

"Well, yes, in a way, only in this case the Pope is a priest and the Vatican is a Foundation," he replied.

"Don't get it," said Ovid.

"I don't either, not all of it," replied Bishop Chatworthy as he glanced at his watch. "Must be on my way. Lots of wrongs to right today."

"Me, too. So long, Excellency."

Alfred Chatworthy was greeted at the Diocesan Office with a welcoming scowl from Mr. Perse, the Treasurer of the Diocese, who would undoubtedly have some unanswerable questions for him after the morning mail.

"Bishop, it's good to have you back," exclaimed Miss Penelope Platen. "I expect that you're all rested up after two weeks with the bishops and ready to get a lot of work done. There's lots of mail."

"There always is," observed the Bishop as he adjusted the venetian blinds, and identified the letter on top of the pile on the desk as that troublesome one from the Senior Warden of St. Lethargus' at Sunken Heights. He recalled that he had delayed answering it in the hope that he would return from Mapleton with the answer given to him from a metropolitan bishop who answered such letters all day long. Instead of receiving an answer, he was asked what he did about this kind of situation.

Within an hour he had completed his correspondence, except that blasted letter from Sunken Heights and another one asking for a marriage judgment for Vicki Snicker whose father was the president of Snoremore Pharmaceutical Laboratories, manufacturer of aids and comforts for today's businessman. "Whifferton at St. Lascivia's knows full well this decree hasn't been final a year yet. And I don't think I can give it then. In her case, it's only the triumph of hope over experience, anyway." He felt a little better after this silent pontificating and called for Miss Platen.

"Penelope," he began, in an episcopal tone, "I have about decided to have a P.L.C., only not quite, but a D.L.C. instead."

"A what?" the astounded Miss Platen asked.

"D.L.C.—Diocesan Life Conference. Never heard of it? Neither have I. I propose to invent one. My quasi-stationary equilibria have been disturbed by this lab and I propose to do something about it," the Bishop announced to his secretary and all the empty chairs at the Executive Council table.

"Well, they certainly have," agreed Miss Platen. "Shall I call Dr. Pilldowner for an appointment?"

"What does he know about D.L.C.'s, Miss Platen? I'm serious, and in my right mind, too."

Leaning back in his chair and interlocking his fingers behind his head and gazing ceilingwards, the Bishop remarked, "I've been thinking again, Penelope."

"Oh, no, what now?" from Miss Platen with resigned alarm.

"The day that I left, I signed letters dimissory for the Reverend J. Walter Tarp to the Diocese of Amazonia. Remember, he was at St. Lethargus' parish at Sunken Heights? I got to thinking about that on my way to the conference and realized that they have had three men in four years, and each of them fine young men, too, although Father Censable used more ceremonial than they would tolerate for long. Come to think of it, Mr. Scarph, who succeeded Censable, didn't use enough. Tarp was just right, and yet they made it difficult for him, especially after he baptized that man and his family who ran the local Rendering Works. Now they say they want an older man. I suppose I could send them Alaric Donebetter, but they wouldn't like his wife. She isn't lovely—as they said about the wives of the three other priests I have sent there."

"And they won't hope he'll stay, either, the way they did the other men. Mr. Donebetter can be difficult," interposed Miss Platen reflectively.

"Miss Platen, I think that I am about to invent a way that might cure this kind of problem without my getting blamed if it doesn't work," the Bishop ruminated. "I am going to give that congregation, and every other one in the Diocese, too, for that matter, a chance to get a good look at themselves. We are going to have psycho-drama and everything."

"We have that around here all the time anyway, especially when you are trying to sell some young clergyman on St. Lethargus'," retorted Miss Platen.

"Never you mind, Penelope. Get the datebook. We are going to set a date for a Special Diocesan Convention."

"You can't do that, Bishop. It's never been done. Besides there is no money crisis," Miss Platen remonstrated. "What will the Executive Council say?"

"Now, Penelope, you're forgetting who the Bishop is around here. It says in the Canon that I can call a Special Convention when there is a need, and I say there is a need around here—with places that can't keep a man. Get my datebook."

Miss Platen, uncertain as to how to deal with this man who had been so genial, kindly, and gentle until his recent trip East, brought the appointment book.

"How about September 25-27? Is that time clear? It would be a good date. Sunday Schools will be organized and limping along. The Every Member Canvass will be a month away. Ideal time," he mused.

Miss Platen answered immediately, "That's the meeting date for the 5th District of the General Division of Women's Work at Moose Nose. You are scheduled for a meditation on, 'Over Philistia will I cast out my shoes.' "

The Bishop groaned. "I can't even pick out my texts. All right, what about October 3-5?"

"Won't do," clipped Miss Platen. "There will be a visiting missionary from Wayoutland in the Diocese all week, and you are to drive him around."

"How nice. And who worked that out?" Alfred retorted, as he realized that he had a real problem finding a suitable time. "Well, then, October 10-12. I am certain that there aren't any diocesan doings then."

"Now, Bishop, you made a date last March to address the

state convention of Antelope Clubs at Lonesome Owl Lodge in the Park. . . ."

The Bishop brightened. "That would make a good place for Convention, wouldn't it? I would know where the clergy were at night in a place as remote as that." He rubbed his hands in self-congratulation of the idea. "I'll write New York and let *them* set a date. The time will have to suit the availability of a leader anyway. Then I'll just call a Convention for the date they give. Penelope, it isn't any fun being a bishop unless I can do as I please once in a while. Take a letter to the Reverend Roger Mixwell—Dear Groupy: . . ."

The days went by swiftly for the Bishop. Over the weekend he took the train to the Air Force Base at Powerdive, arriving there just in time to see a plane taking off. "There goes your Confirmation class, Bishop," said the Commanding Officer. "They're off to Viet Nam." He called his old friend, Albert Boswell, at Dry Wells to come over and drive him there for the weekend.

The Church of the Insurrection at Dry Wells had grown and prospered under the patient ten-year rectorship of Boswell. He had been at Dry Wells long enough to have buried many of the "obstructionists in the redemptive enterprise," as Albert phrased it, adding for the Bishop's benefit that having buried half the congregation, firing the other half, and building a new congregation around the remnant, he was staying right there. Dry Wells suited his spirit. It also suited the Bishop, for the community, an oasis on the plains, was a large enough town to stave off boredom and small enough to provide leisure and fishing, yet keeping men happy in such places was a major problem. The Bishop had reflected many times on the incongruity of a man's preparing for the ordained ministry by spending three years in a seminary in a metropolitan center, picking a city girl for a wife, and then coming sight unseen into the cultural desert to do heroic deeds for the Kingdom.

Most candidates, he believed, had been changed into blacktop and neon men by the time they finished their studies. He was thankful for men like Albert, his friend from seminary days. In return for loyalty and good works, Albert could do much as he pleased, which included giving Chatworthy advice when it wasn't asked for.

As dinner was finished, Boswell brought up the subject of the Special Convention. "Alfred, just what are you trying to

"There goes your Confirmation class, Bishop . . . They're off for Viet Nam."

do? The Dewberry crowd got hold of you, didn't they? and they're passing off Roger Mixwell on you, besides."

"Bert, I've been grouped," announced the Bishop, "victimized by the force-field principle, washed in the blood of the lab, and elected quarterback for our T group." He continued baiting his friend, "And I shall be restless until I have done everything that I can to heal the person-hurt from which all our dear people suffer." Turning from the pleasure of annoying Boswell, he continued more seriously, "I came across something in that whole business which will upset every ecclesiastical apple cart in the Diocese and loosen the death grip that certain individuals in many congregations have which keeps these places in chronic suffocation."

"I still think you're way out, Alfred. It will just compound the problem. Besides, you'll have to face them all singly and answer for it. It's easier to wait them out and bury them," concluded Albert.

"Takes too long. The congregations keep getting smaller all the time. It's getting more difficult to provide men every year. These places all have reputations as clergy-killers. No priest with a choice would ever go there. I'm required to send men right out of school as a lamb amidst wolves." He paused for a moment. "Bert, would you go to Sunken Heights?"

Albert waved his hand in silent scorn.

"Of course you wouldn't. I'd like to be able to go there for about six months. I'd sever a few heads so neatly that they wouldn't know it until they sneezed."

After that pronouncement, Chatworthy leaned back, pleased with his conviction and witness. Boswell could see that his friend had the bit in his teeth and knew that there was nothing that he could do to deter him now. Earlier, he had decided to avoid the whole business by planning some critical sicknesses and a couple of burials which would interfere, but he changed his mind when he saw what Chatworthy had let himself in for. "He'll need me there to hold off some of those dragons who will really be out for his blood. I wish he'd stick to bishopping. He's good at that," Boswell privately mused as he put on his coat to go over to the church to check on the Altar Guild before turning in.

Boswell's parting words to the Bishop as he took him to the train on Sunday night had little effect. He could see that he was set on going to his destruction. "The weight of office is beginning to tell on him," he suspected. "He used to be easy to talk to as a Bishop, but now he's beginning to act like all the rest of them. He sets his mind and that's all there is to it. Suppose I could get some laymen to put the pressure on him. They can do more with a Bishop than a priest can, anyway." He abandoned the whole idea and resignedly bade Alfred farewell.

The Bishop returned to Hereford in time for a Monday meeting with the group leaders who had been appointed to give their all in the new experiment in curing the Church's ills. The clergy had done their job well. Everyone responded and seemed enthusiastic except Mrs. Fillmore Bowles, the Diocesan President of the Cousins of Perpetua (Virgin and Martyr), who expressed blanket disapproval.

"A waste of time, Bishop. Besides, the women in each parish and mission are busy getting ready for their bazaars."

The Bishop held his tongue as he reflected to himself that if it wasn't the bazaars, they were getting ready for a rummage sale or a pancake supper.

Bishop Chatworthy made a visitation to St. Arachne's, Webb Center, over the weekend prior to the Convention. He confirmed five young girls, and, after a coffee hour, met with the Vestry on the subject of the rector's salary. The Warden concluded with the depressing observation that attendance at services was falling off and the income was declining as a result.

"Then, too, Bishop, we've been talking all this over and feel that we need a more forward-looking man, and yet one that has a certain dignity about him. As an example, the other day Father Nosworthy was in the supermart wearing levis and a sweat shirt. Now don't get me wrong, Bishop, I wear 'em myself, but all this causes talk and reflects on my church and I think you ought to do something about it."

"Like what," reflected Alfred to himself, "design a clerical collar for a sweat shirt and steam press levis?" He let it pass and brought the subject around to the Convention. "I expect that I'll see you all at Lonesome Owl Lodge next week."

"What's going on up there?" asked Howe Noble, the Junior Warden.

"Why, Special Convention of the Diocese," said the Bishop.

"If you ask me, I think there are too many meetings," cut in Claude Footweaver, who, as his contribution to the life of the parish, played the organ in place of a pledge.

Ignoring Footweaver's statement, the Bishop asked, "Who are the delegates from St. Arachne's?"

James Wright, the Clerk, announced apologetically that the parish would not be represented. Casting about for reasons, he repeated some that had been given to him by those who chose to stay at home. "The bowling league starts this week and that rules out Charles Striker and his wife. Then there's PTA organizational meeting on Wednesday with a speaker from the state office." He brightened momentarily as he thought of the main reason. "On Wednesday and Thursday nights, the Paternal Order of Mystic Wahoo is having ritual drill team competition. This is some town, all right, something going on all the time," the Clerk observed. "We just don't have anybody that can make it up to the Fulsome Fowl Lodge."

"Lonesome Owl, Mr. Wright," corrected the Bishop. "I was in hopes that each congregation would be well represented as we attempt to tackle the problems which confront us in the congregations and in the Diocese."

99

Howe Noble broke in, "There's nothing wrong here, Bishop, that a good minister couldn't correct. As I see it, that's our problem."

Chatworthy showed a little irritation. "Now, Howe, congregations get just the kind of a man that they deserve in most cases." He paused for the Vestry to come out of shock. "Where do we get our clergymen? From the laity, that's where. And do you know what laity? Mostly from other Christian bodies—men who have come into the Church, gone to seminary, received Holy Orders, and are now serving the Lord in our midst. And do you know why over half of our priests are from other churches? Because we don't produce our own. How many has St. Arachne's given to the Church? None, that's how many—and in seventy-three years. Don't blame the clergy overmuch, Howe. We are all to blame. You want another rector. As the French say, a change is just the same thing. I may make a few changes, but until we cease all this silliness about the clergy, the same conditions will continue to prevail." The Bishop was surprised to hear himself talk this frankly and heatedly. It wasn't like him. During the deathlike silence that followed, he gathered his aplomb.

"My wife's waiting in the car. Guess I better go," said John Wright.

"Me, too," agreed Noble. "Take you anywhere, Bishop?"

"Nosworthy will be here in a few minutes to take me to dinner. You men go right ahead. I know that you have other obligations."

In this and other ways, the Bishop saw that there would have to be a mighty working of the Spirit if the Special Convention was going to bring any change in the Diocese. He worked hard all week, urging, prodding, cajoling, in order to ensure a high percentage of parish representation, and finally the day arrived.

"Come on, Kathleen, I'm ready," called the Bishop from the hallway to his wife who was still upstairs gathering up the fragments. "I want to get to Lonesome Owl Lodge early enough to tend to several matters."

"I'll be there in a minute. I'm putting the laundry away. Don't rush me," she called back. His lordship sat on the lower step with patience, cleaned his fingernails, and retied his shoes. He arose and sauntered to the piano and fingered a tune faintly reminiscent of "I Don't Know Why I Love You Like I Do."

"That's enough of that, Alfred. You're just trying to soften me up. Go on out and start the car. I'll be right down," her voice trailed away as she went into the back bedroom. The Bishop made his way to the garage, backed the Eocene 6 out, and drew up alongside the curb. Shortly after he had resignedly turned off the motor, Kathleen popped out of the door like a cork out of a bottle.

"You're always rushing me, and I don't like it," she started.

"I'm always waiting, and I don't like that, either."

"You can afford to wait. You don't have to get the house in order for Mrs. Starkey to come into to take care of the tribe," she retorted.

The usual and habitual repartee, long since staled out, drifted into silence until they drove through East Felony. "Better slow up, Alfred," she warned, "you know how well this street is patrolled."

At that moment the familiar siren sounded and the Bishop dutifully pulled over to the curb and dug in his wallet for his driver's license.

"You agin, Reverend?" greeted the officer. "Sorry, but I'm gonna have to cite ya. You're always going too fast."

"I've been supporting the forces of law and order here regularly, officer. Any chance of a pass?"

"Now you know I can't do that. Here's your ticket, and take it easy, will ya?"

"I wish you'd obey the law. You're always talking about it, you know," reminded Kathleen.

"I wish that these fines were tax deductible, that's what I wish. I am playing a useful role in society by keeping that cop on the alert," replied Alfred.

"Officer of the law, you mean," corrected his wife. "Don't let that priest up in Red Cliff hear you call an officer a 'cop.' "

"Father Derringer is always correcting me. He even assumes, just like any cop, yes, I said 'cop,' that I am guilty until proved innocent. It's getting these days to where a man can't even violate a little law just a little bit without being cited," the Bishop grumbled on.

Shifting the subject, Kathleen opened a new gambit. "Just what are you trying to accomplish by this Special Convention? I haven't seen you recently long enough to find out."

"Now, Kathleen, I know what I'm doing," the Bishop answered defensively. He never could come up immediately with the right answers to her questions.

"I know you do, dear," she responded sympathetically. "After twenty-five years with you, I have never found you without an answer yet. I just want to know the answer to this one."

"As you know, I have been nagged at and nibbled at for years to get 'good' priests for the mission fields and small parishes. No matter whom I get, these places never stay happy with them for long. There is something wrong with the congregations. Not even I could be wrong so consistently. There were a lot of good men who have gone through this diocese on their way in the life of the Church, and many of them amounted to something, too. I propose to get at the problem by throwing these people together and letting them ventilate, without any clerics being in on their group. I am doing it in the hope and with the faith that they will stumble across their own derelictions." The Bishop paused for breath and waited for rebuttal.

Alfred was surprised and pleased to hear his wife's ready

agreement with his findings. Her only doubt was the question of whether it would really work.

"It worked personally on the Bishop of Fanfare at that Group Life Lab. You should have seen the old boy steam up in our T group. He took everything personally, I think mainly because there wasn't any way he could get at us; we all have our own jurisdictions. I found out one thing about him, though. He feels that he is a threatened man. I should think that he would, what with that Standing Committee he has to battle with and some of those laymen who think they are paying the bills." He paused for a moment to pass a truck. "I came around to be pretty good friends with him. Never got next to him before. I wouldn't have his job. . . ."

"Alfred, we were talking about the Convention. How is this one going to be run?" Kathleen inquired.

"Believe it or not, I am not making any speeches, not even a sermon. I'm not even going to chair anything."

"That I'll have to see. You have to express an opinion on every subject."

"The Convention is set up in such a way that I can't—and I consented to it," he proudly added.

"It will be a great day for the Church," Kathleen replied, with a twist of the needle.

"Touché! O.K., Kathleen. Listen carefully as I divulge the mysteries of the dark plot about to be hatched. Mixwell from New York is going to run the thing. There will be about three hundred laymen there, and all of the clergy. He divides them into groups of about ten, each with a leader. I pulled a fast one, too. I put the clergy in separate groups so that the laymen will have a chance to get a word in. Boy! Will they give me the business in that first session." He chuckled at the thought of it.

"Alfred, your clergy will just shred you to bits for this," warned his wife.

"I know, my dear, but I have the utmost confidence that the force-field principle will work this time like it always has done," the Bishop explained, "and besides that, the Convention opens on Friday, and there are enough fasting clergy to prevent such an impious act."

"The *what* principle?" she asked, ignoring what Alfred thought was a clever witticism.

"Why don't you get grouped, like me, then you will be educated and have all the answers yourself?" taunted Alfred.

Kathleen rose to the challenge. "You've gone social dynamics cult," she accused him.

"I have not . . . Where did you get the lingo?" he asked suspiciously.

"I know some things. And I know there are some things that you don't want me to know," she goaded. "You wouldn't send me to a Group Life Lab. That would mean that you would have to be home with the children too long." It was a telling blow.

"Now, Kathleen, you know that the demands of this work require that I be available all the time."

"So you've told me before," she said, enjoying his discomfort.

"I have arranged for you to go on the Women's Retreat next month, haven't I?" he countered.

"You're a noble soul, m'lord, but I think that the only reason you want me on that retreat is because you know that it's cheaper than a psychiatrist. Being married to the Bishop of Blunderland is a marginal occupation at best." She left him bleeding as they drove on in silence.

"Remarkable woman," pondered Alfred as they drove up the road to the Lonesome Owl Lodge.

X

Onward, Convention Delegates

TIME CAME for the opening service of the Special Diocesan Convention in the splendid new hall at Lonesome Owl Lodge. Alfred always loved these large services. The singing was joyful and full. Everyone caught the spirit. "Going to be kerygma all over the place, tonight, Dean," he predicted as the clergy took their places in procession. Evensong went well. The only part that dragged was the second lesson read by Alaric Donebetter. It took him nearly eleven minutes to get through Stephen's sermon in the Book of Acts. The Bishop fidgeted. (*"I should have assigned the lessons. That man invariably picks out the long wrong ones."*) Finally, he heard the words of release, "Here endeth the Second Lesson." The congregation visibly sighed and shifted. Alfred secretly had an unholy thought, *"If Stephen preached the way Alaric reads, no wonder he was stoned."*

After giving a few words of welcome, the Bishop resumed his seat, and Dr. Pilldowner, the prominent layman from St. Mitre's, Sedalia, made the address. The man did remarkably well, the Bishop thought; he even left his manuscript up in his room. It really was refreshing, but Alfred suspected that the clergy thought they could improve on it. With the closing hymn, "Come, Labour On," all filed out, and filled the air with talk and cigarette smoke. Bishop Chatworthy was cornered by the Reverend Wordsworth Little of St. Juniper's,

Smallwood, when he heard Mixwell bring the gavel down, calling the convention to order.

When preliminary announcements and explanations were made, the Reverend Mr. Mixwell proceeded to call out the names of members of the various groups and where they would meet.

"The Clergy Group One will meet in the Tepee Room. Clergy Group Two will meet in the Moccasin Room—Miss Mimi O'Graf will let you in with the key. Clergy Group Three will meet in the Lewis & Clark Lounge." Groans, laughs, and cheers greeted victims as names for each group were read. Mr. Mixwell went on in his cheerful voice. "Laymen. Group One, Agate Room, new addition. Listen carefully. Here are the names: Harvey Quiverlip, St. Lethargus', Sunken Heights; John Saddler, Insurrection, Dry Wells; Mrs. Nikki Summers, St. Eclampsia's, Horse Meadow; Mr. Harry Rosewell, St. Laodicea's, Luke Springs; Mrs. Herman Grimm, Trinity, Clinkerton; John Hillman, St. Angus' Cathedral, Hereford; Captain Martin, St. Ariel's, Powerdive; Mr. Watts Dewing, St. Juniper's, Smallwood; Mrs. Griselda Galsworthy III, Grace Church, Ardmore."

As they rose to meet in their appointed places, the Bishop noted with dismay, and some misgiving, the startling lineup of personality in the Agate Room group. He motioned to John Hillman of the Cathedral.

"Good luck, John, you have a real bunch of tartars. Get them at each other as quickly as you can. They will murder me first and then the clergy. Make it as painless as possible," counselled the Bishop, feeling, now that it was too late, that perhaps he had been a bit hasty and should have listened to his good friend the Rector of Dry Wells. John Hillman just smiled and followed the group out the door. "Praise be to God," breathed the Bishop. "He's the only man to handle that gang."

Group number one, temporarily entangled with milling and

grumbling clergy, made their way down the hall to their room and found their chairs calculatedly placed in a circle, the right number, too, strangely enough. John Hillman rapped for order.

"Ladies and gentlemen," he began, "for better, for worse, it has fallen your lot to have me as Group Leader for these sessions. My apologies in advance for my clumsiness which sooner or later will be demonstrated."

"You mean we're going to have to sit around in this room all day tomorrow, too?" demanded Mrs. Galsworthy. "The Bishop knows full well that I have better use of my time."

"Mrs. Galsworthy," began Mr. Hillman, "I am sure that if this were to be fruitless the Bishop would not ask us to endure. However, let us see how it goes first. Then maybe I'll walk out with you." With this polite reassurance, he established himself in a way that would have pleased the Bishop of Blunderland. He resumed, "Now I think that it will make us all a little less self-conscious and help up to become acquainted if we in turn introduce ourselves and identify our parish or mission."

"My name's Quiverlip," volunteered Harvey. "I'm Clerk of the Vestry at St. Lethargus', Sunken Heights.

"John Saddler, Dry Wells. Ran my term out as Vestryman a year ago, so now all I do is give advice to Father Boswell and take up space in the nickel seats," volunteered John, leaning back in his chair and displaying a pair of expensive cowboy boots.

"I'm Nikki Summers from Horse Meadows," spoke up the delegate from St. Eclampsia's. "I just love conventions. People are so interesting." Attired in red toreador pants and a white sweater, she was, too, judging from the assessing gazes of the men.

"And now, you, sir," said Hillman, cutting in and diverting attention from Mrs. Summers.

"Name's Harry Rosewell, Secretary of the Chamber of

Commerce in Luke Springs. You know, St. Laodicea's Church. Wordsworth Little's our Vicar and a fine fellow. Better all come over for Pioneer Days. Start growing your whiskers early and you ladies work on your mustaches."

A look of disapproval went around the room and ended on Mrs. Galsworthy's face with a wince.

"Next."

"Mrs. Herman Grimm. I come from Trinity Church in Clinkerton. My husband, Herman, he's in the Men's Club. I don't know much about this stuff, but I come because the pastor ask me."

"And we are pleased that he did, Mrs. Grimm," put in Hillman, which relaxed her three chins and produced a self-conscious smile.

"Captain Martin from St. Ariel's at the Powerdive Air Base, and I want everyone at ease," he volunteered.

An easing laugh went round the group.

"And my name is Watts Dewing, Warden at St. Juniper's, Smallwood. When Mister Little isn't being kept busy over at Luke Springs, he comes over to take services for us."

"Whad'y'mean, Dewing? He's over in Smallwood all the time," countered Harry Rosewell. "What are ya' doin', feedin' him chicken?"

"Gentlemen," cut in Hillman, "I think we had better get on, although Mrs. Galsworthy hardly needs an introduction, being the grandame of the parish in Ardmore, and indeed of the Diocese."

Mrs. Galsworthy acknowledged the introduction gracefully with a "Good evening," and returned to her scrutiny of the group.

"And now, ladies and gentlemen," resumed John Hillman, "I believe that we are ready to begin. I have been instructed that there is no agenda but the one that we make for ourselves. We may discuss anything we wish and no reports given to anyone."

The short silence was broken by Mrs. Galsworthy, "You mean that the Bishop is just having us sit in here making noises at each other?"

"I don't get his angle," probed Harry Rosewell. " 'Course he isn't much of a planner or promoter, anyway. Now if I was doin' it. . . ."

"There must be some reason to bring us all this distance," said Nikki Summers, searching for a reason.

"The Bishop never needs a reason for what he does. He's always been that way," supplied Watts Dewing suspiciously. "He's got an angle all right, you can count on that old fox."

"I resent your speaking of our Bishop that way, Mr. Rosewell, even if I don't like guessing games," defended Mrs. Galsworthy III.

"Seems to me that he could put his time to better use getting clergymen who would stay in the churches," observed John Saddler. "Now, I don't have a complaint. Our priest has been there ten years, but I remember how it used to be before Boswell decided to settle down in Dry Wells."

"In defense of the bishop, I would like to say that he sent us three men in three years at St. Lethargus'," spoke up Harvey Quiverlip. "They were fine young men and they all had lovely wives and and we all hoped that they would stay, but they didn't."

"You know, he just sent us the nicest young minister at Horse Meadows," crowed Nikki Summers. "Ronnie Goodfellow is his name. We all call him Father Ronnie, and he is so busy working with the youth and making new signs for the church that he couldn't come to convention. He is just a dear and so is his wife. I just know they are going to stay."

"I see no cause for going after the Bishop," said Captain Martin. "He's got a tough assignment. Last week he came all the way to Powerdive and found the Confirmation class had all been transferred to Viet Nam. No one thought to call him, including me," he added apologetically.

John Hillman interrupted, "Mrs. Grimm, everyone has had something to say but you. Would you like to give an opinion?"

Mrs. Grimm shifted around in her chair. "Well, my Herman, he reads the papers and he knows what's going on and he likes the Bishop fine. I do, too. My Herman knows, he does."

Mrs. Grimm's forced comment proved to be the real conversation-stopper on the premature post-mortem of the Bishop of Blunderland. John Hillman began again by casting a few lines into the rippling stream just above the cascades.

"Mr. Rosewell," began Hillman, "I think that you said a moment ago that your Vicar is shared with the congregation at Smallwood. At least I gathered that from your remark to Mr. Dewing."

"Sharing isn't the word. We provide a house, heat, and utilities, and pay nine hundred dollars toward his salary, and never see him except on Sundays," replied Harry.

"Wait a minute, Harry," cut in Dewing, "we're paying him twelve hundred dollars and his mileage. Mr. Little comes over on Wednesdays for service and calling and instruction classes, and he comes over again on Sundays for services after you're through with him. With him living over at Luke Springs, we don't think we're getting our money's worth."

Mrs. Nikki Summers watched the interplay like a spectator at a tennis match. "You mean that between your two places the poor parson only gets $2100, a place to live, and some little things?"

"Oh, no," explained Rosewell, "the Diocese kicks in another $1900 to make it come up to $4000."

"Doesn't the Bishop have something to say about the distribution of work, as long as he's paying half the bill?" asked Captain Martin.

Dewing answered by saying that the Bishop left them alone, except that he appointed a Vicar. "Of course," he added,

110

Mrs. Nikki Summers watched the interplay like a spectator at a tennis match.

"that's a good deal for the Bishop. He dumps men on us that no place else would take."

"Now, just a minute, young man," interrupted Griselda Galsworthy III. "The Reverend L. Sewickley Codger, Rector of Grace Church, came to this Diocese ten years ago when our Bishop was elected. His first charge was the very one you are discussing. He remained among you for two years and received a call to be Rector of Grace Church. Dr. Codger was not 'dumped' on you, as you phrase it. And may I remind you that you have had four men since then, and Mr. Wordsworth Little won't be there long, I wager."

"I apologize, Mrs. Galsworthy," acknowledged Mr. Rosewell, "I didn't mean it the way it sounded. It always seems that if we could just get the right man, then we could expand and we wouldn't need to share a man with Smallwood."

"You know, Harry," ruminated Watts Dewing, "if you could get that gang over there at Luke Springs to start giving, you might be able to get one on your own. There's lots of money over there, where our people just don't have it."

"Now wait a minute, Dewing," rebutted Rosewell. "You got that all backwards. You live in the town that's loaded. St. Juniper's, Smallwood, shouldn't have any problems."

Dewing, in silent scorn, waved Rosewell's argument away. Hillman attempted to spread out the conversation.

"Mrs. Grimm, how long as Father Swemp been at Clinkerton?"

She replied carefully, "My Herman says that we have had five pastors in forty years and he thinks we have good ones, and we have a good parish. My Herman knows."

"No more there," thought Hillman. He tried again.

"Mr. Saddler, you have had a discouraging history until the Reverend Albert Boswell came to you. What changed things so that he wanted to stay?" Hillman felt that he had a good one on the line, now.

"The Church of the Insurrection used to be a real preacher-

112

killer. Rougher'n a cob on young fellows. Usually took the parish about six months to get a new rector up a tree. Got to be kind of a game. Then this man, Boswell, came along. He chased our troublemakers up trees instead. Bert told me, after he'd been there for awhile, that he was going to wait out a few burials and get on with the job of being a priest and not paying any attention to 'em. Took him about five years to soften up that bunch. They couldn't budge him. They took to writing the Bishop who answered their letters and never said a thing in the reply. They gradually began to see that Bert's idea of what the Church should be doing was different. Stories began getting around about how he helped this person and that. He got a lotta static from it at first because some of the old buzzards around the town wanted the preacher to be their private chaplain. Bert didn't go for that a'tall, and he told 'em so. They tried to starve him out but some of us rougher cattlemen got behind him and helped him pay his bills on the side. Then, too, a couple of times the Bishop chipped in. Nobody could figure how Boswell could hang on. Pretty soon he had all the town on his side against the parish, and that was the end of that. Now he has things pretty much his own way."

Harvey Quiverlip was in deep thought. He stirred during Saddler's testimony as if getting up courage to speak. Finally, he straightened up, was acknowledged by Hillman, and began, "You know, we've gone through three men in less than four years over at Sunken Heights. From what Mr. Saddler has been saying, I can see that our people have been doing the same thing. I felt guilty about letting J. Walter Tarp go. He was a fine young man, and he had a lovely wife."

Mrs. Galsworthy commented, "Harvey, I know that your parish has a reputation for being hard on young men. It has that reputation all over the Diocese. None of our own men will go there. The Bishop has to sell an outsider on it every time. He has told me so many times. I wonder, is there anything we can do about . . .?"

Just then the bell rang. Hillman announced, "That's all for tonight, ladies and gentlemen. This has been most enlightening, certainly for me, and I am sure for all of us. When we meet tomorrow, we may go on from here, or take any turn that we wish. Think it over and we'll check reactions when we meet again after the early service and breakfast."

They all filed out and mingled with the crowd to find their fellow delegates and friends. Everyone appeared to be in the same spirit of preoccupation. "It's working!" gleefully thought the Bishop.

With coffee-breaks between sessions, and two hours off for lunch, Convention moved into high gear the following day. Nor was Bishop Chatworthy idle. Miss Platen had made up an interview schedule, marked off in fifteen minute intervals and taped it to the door of the room labeled "Bear Pit." Four times each hour the apostolic lion of Judah was bearded in his den. "I felt like a lion in a cageful of Daniels," he commented to his wife afterwards. All that he could remember of that strenuous day was that morning began with direct questions such as, "Bishop, what are you going to do about Father Stickney?" "What are you going to do about the assessment at St. Lethargus'?" "What are you going to do about Camp Wob-a-lee?" In the afternoon, he recalled that the nature of the questions began to change. "Bishop, our man is falling behind in paying his bills. What should we do?" "Bishop, how can we spike the Frothinghams over at St. Donald's?" "Bishop, what do you think we should do about our financial situation?" Things were looking up indeed. Tired and exhausted but with victory in sight, Alfred emerged from his cell to join the final plenary session of the Convention.

The session was called to order by the Reverend Mr. Mixwell: "Ladies and gentlemen," he called out. "I shall try to make this as brief and painless as possible. The leader of each group has prepared a statement of what has been going on among them. (*Laughter.*) These statements will now be presented, without confidences being divulged. (*Nervous laughter.*) It is our hope that we shall thus be able, in our several ways, to carry the insights and experiences back into our parishes and missions so that our Church may be the force in the community that she is expected to be. We shall begin by hearing the report from Clergy Group Number One."

The Reverend Phineas Holihill rose and faced the convention. "We wish first of all to apologize to His Lordship, the Bishop of Blunderland, for our lack of faith in this inspiring experience that he has made possible for all of us. We talked over many matters which I fear would be regarded as shop talk, churchmanship, ceremonial, and how to discipline the laity." (Alfred winced when Albert Boswell caught his eye.) "In closing, may I state that the unanimous opinion of our group is their desire that the Bishop be freed from many of his labors so that he may be able to devote himself more fully to being our Father-in-God. Thank you."

L. Sewickley Codger asked for the floor. "Right Reverend Sir, Mr. Chairman, Delegates. I am grasping this slender opportunity to present in a sentence the minority report of one, who would amend the final resolution of the Reverend Phineas Holihill to read: that the Bishop be freed from many of his labors so that he may be able to devote himself more fully to being our Grandfather-in-God." His comment brought down the house. Mr. Mixwell rapped and called for order. Codger triumphantly returned to his seat smiling indulgently at the younger members of the group that he had endured for a day and a night.

Mr. Mixwell began, "Mrs. Fillmore Bowles has requested that Group Number Seven's report be given at this time inasmuch as she must leave immediately to chair the monthly meeting of the Cousins of Perpetua at St. Hyacinth's, Ambrosia. Mrs. Bowles, the floor is yours."

"We had quite a time getting started, as I am sure the rest of you did," began Mrs. Bowles. "I attempted to keep the discussion on constructive levels of organization and finance, but we did get sidetracked, didn't we?" She smiled over the top of her generous bosom. "The entire group voiced the opinion that the clergy were called away from their work too frequently for conferences and retreats, and the like. It was felt that we should state an objection officially to this condition with the hope that this Convention may take some action which would reduce their traveling about when they ought to be in their parishes, calling, and conducting meetings, and the like. I so move, Mr. Chairman, and would be happy to serve on any committee appointed to inquire further into the matter." Mrs. Bowles dabbed at her upper lip as she plodded down the aisle to the door and homeward to the meeting of the Cousins of Perpetua (Virgin and Martyr).

The Reverend Albert Boswell indicated a desire for the floor, which was granted. "Right Reverend Sir, Mr. Chairman, Delegates. While not a member of this group, and realizing that I am out of order, which I have been given to understand is usually the case (*laughter*), I have a comment to make in connection with this report because I don't believe the subject will come up again. Seriously, there should be no objection to priests absent for good reason. As you all know, we have a large number of young men, the Dean, Doctor Codger, and myself excluded. (*laughter*.) To add to the problem, we compound inexperience with isolation. That is to say, we, in the Diocese of Blunderland are off the main stream of the life of the Church, geographically. Our Bishop is well aware of our situation and is constantly bringing leaders from all parts of the Church to us so that we may keep abreast of what is going on. Our problems would be much worse were it not for his foresight. This is a Diocese where young men come to make their mistakes before returning to the East. Whatever can be done to reduce this unhappy state of affairs should have our full support."

There was a murmuring throughout the hall as Albert concluded his pointed remarks, accompanied by hostile heckling by the junior curates and their satellites. It didn't bother an old campaigner like Albert. He wore many ecclesiastical scars.

Mr. Mixwell eased the tension before proceeding. "Perhaps Father Boswell would like to be turned over, like St. Lawrence, so that he could be barbecued on the other side." Laughter of relief followed and everybody smiled at Albert, none more broadly than the Bishop. "We must press onward and upward, delegates," Mixwell pursued. "We shall now hear from Group Number One of the laity."

John Hillman, erect and purposeful, strode to the rostrum. "Right Reverend Sir," (with a slight bow to the Bishop), "Mr. Chairman, and Delegates. It has been an enlightening and edifying experience to have had the privilege of chairing this group. When we had carried off the dead and wounded after the first round (*laughter*), our group moved on to some sound and honest observations and recommendations, only the chief of which I shall report at this time, inasmuch as I understand that the full printed reports will be available in a few days from the Diocesan Office." He turned to the report. "We dealt with the problem of short clergy tenure in small parishes and missions. Admittedly, it was from our point of view, but we did make a sustained and sincere effort to look at the phenomenon from the clergyman's perspective as well." Hillman had them listening carefully to every word. "We discovered a strong desire on the part of our people to stay as they are and a reluctance to face up to the fact that we have a mission to fulfill in our communities. We detected that many of our people insisted primarily on the clergyman being an Episcopal chaplain. Much of the difficulty, we felt, was due to the laity pulling one way in an attempt to keep the church a private chapel, and the clergy pulling the other way. The basic problem, we are convinced, lies not necessarily in communication but in understanding. Conflicting ideas get in our way more than the words do. Our people have one idea of the nature and function of the Church, and the clergy have another. I shall not go further into this matter now, but have a resolution to present to this body."

With a nod from Mixwell, John Hillman proceeded, "Whereas, in this Convention assembled for the purpose of recovering the mission of the Church, and discovering how better we may serve the Lord, we do hereby respectfully submit the following resolution: Therefore, be it resolved that the Bishop, through the Executive Council, encourage conferences of this kind in every parish and mission in the Diocese during the coming year in order to achieve greater unanimity of understanding whereby we may develop a program and strategy by which the Church may serve in her rightful capacity in this Diocese."

Hillman motioned a "thank you" and returned to his place. Immediately several people rose to their feet and demanded the floor. The resolution caught on and was acclaimed. The Bishop went out to the coke machine.

"Well, Alfred," said Boswell, who followed him out, "you got your way again, didn't you? I'll have to admit that I didn't think that you could carry it off."

"You always did underestimate me, Bert," chided the Bishop.

"Come off it. You've been saying that for years. Probably some basic insecurity. Didn't your mother ever approve of you?" Bert regretted his outburst for a moment, but was relieved to see his friend chuckling.

"Nothing can disturb him now," thought Albert, "he looks like the canary that chased the cat up a tree."

The Bishop shifted to Hillman's words. "You know, Bert, I haven't thought about it overmuch, but Hillman put his finger right on the problem in a way that I didn't expect. All we hear these days is that the trouble is one of communication. I hope Mixwell picked up the idea. It isn't communication. It's understanding, and it takes charity and patience to have that."

As the Bishop and Bert Boswell were enjoying their private prelude to the victory dinner, Mr. Mixwell could be heard adjourning the Convention with the reminder that all would be grouped once more, but this time at the banquet table.

Some of the younger priests, under the wing of Father Holihill, congregated around the fireplace at the far end of the lounge to read Evening Prayer, ostentatiously, with much crossing of breasts and surreptitious eyeing of each other for coordination of the risings up and sittings down. Across the room was a mixed group of clerics and young couples engaged in bursts of laughter at witticism suppressed during the day. The Bishop went to his room to freshen up for the banquet. Looking over the lounge, the Reverend Albert Boswell was heard to remark, "Just like any rodeo: the colts frisked and the stallions bucked."

". . . and Balaam's friends brayed," concluded Sewickley Codger, who wished he'd thought of it on convention floor.

XI

Pastor of the Pastors

THE PHONE RANG at five-thirty A.M. Alfred swung his arm across in a wild effort to grab the receiver before it rang again. The infernal machine crashed to the floor. Chatworthy groped for it, found it, pressed it to his ear, and responded with a groggy, "Yes?"

"I apologize about the hour, Bishop, but this is urgent."

"Who is this?" demanded the Bishop impatiently.

It was the Reverend Ralph Goodrich, the new Rector that Alfred had procured for Trinity, Bigview, last Spring. Goodrich hastened to explain that, unbeknown to the Bishop, he was in the hospital convalescing from an appendectomy, but that was not the purpose of his call.

"Bishop," continued Goodrich, "there has been a terrible tragedy down at Sand Springs—you know, about a hundred miles west of Bigview. It's about the Merton family, they're our people there at the Mission."

"Yes, yes, I know. Get on with it. I'm awake," urged the Bishop.

"Jim Merton's daughter and son-in-law have just been murdered by some punk who ran amuck. The year-old baby was also shot and may not live, and Jim's wife, Helen, is here in the hospital—collapsed."

"You want me to come down? Is that it?" asked the Bishop.

"It would sure help, Bishop, especially with no other clergy in this area; but first could you go over to the college in

120

Hereford and talk to Janie? She's the other child, and is in school there. She lives in the dorm. Her Dad already has called the dorm, but they aren't going to tell her until you arrive," explained Ralph.

"No, of course not," thought Alfred, "get the Bishop. He'll do it." He realized that Goodrich was not to blame, though, but that he was trying to see that the Church was on the job when so desperately needed.

"I wish that I could be there, Bishop, but this is only the third day after surgery and I don't think I could make it."

"Of course not, Ralph. I'll get under way and will see you either tonight or tomorrow."

Chatworthy hurriedly dressed and drove over to the girl's dorm at the college. He was met at the door by the Dean of Women.

"Am I ever glad to see you, Bishop!" she exclaimed. "Come in. I have some coffee ready. I'll call Janie." The Dean disappeared down the hall as Chatworthy made his way into the tiny apartment off the entrance to the dormitory. The Bishop heard footsteps coming down the hall and braced himself for the ordeal. Janie appeared in the doorway with a fearful, anxious look.

Alfred arose. "Come in and sit down, Janie. I have some bad news."

"Something happen to mother or dad?" she asked quickly.

"No. It's Lou and Frank. They were shot last night. I don't know any of the details," he repeated slowly.

"Were they badly hurt?"

"They were killed, Jane." A caught breath and a long pause.

"What about the baby? What about him?" she cried.

"He's in the hospital up at Bigview. That's all I know. If you will get dressed, we'll drive home."

It was a long, three-hundred-mile ride to Sand Springs, and

121

a silent one. Alfred left it that way. Twice they were stopped by state troopers who had set up roadblocks through this whole section of the state to cut off the killer, even though no one knew who he was. Several times Alfred noted small planes flying low over the range and canyons searching, ever searching, for one in desperate flight.

There was no one at the tiny house in town. The Bishop and Janie got back into the car and drove to the small business section. It had been blocked off, and men and women were milling about the street, gathered in small groups. It was an uncomfortable feeling, thought Alfred, to see an entire community out, everyone carrying firearms of some sort, and everyone suspecting the other of murder. Janie spied her father coming out of the garage, holding a shotgun, and ran to him.

Chatworthy could find nothing to stay in town for, so he asked Jim and Janie to accompany him to Bigview where Janie's mother and the grandchild were in the hospital.

The nurse at the desk directed Alfred to the correct room. "Lie still, Helen, it's only me," said the Bishop quietly, as he placed his hand on the mother's forehead. "Jim and Janie are with me and will be right in. I'm going to see the baby, then I'll be right back."

Chatworthy reached into the oxygen tent and placed his hand on the little fellow's forehead. "Little Frankie, I lay my hands upon thee in the name of Jesus of Nazareth. Let Thy Healing Presence restore him, Lord." Alfred took the oil stock from his pocket and made the sign of the cross on Frankie's forehead. "I anoint thee with oil in the name of the Father and the Son and the Holy Ghost, beseeching the mercies of God that all sickness and weakness be banished from thee, and the blessings of health be thine. Amen."

He made his way back to Helen. She appeared much comforted by his presence: "Bishop, Frankie hasn't been baptized yet. Seems like with one thing and another, and living way out at the end of nowhere in Sand Springs. . . . If he lives I guess I'm going to have to take care of him, and I'd like to have you baptize him now. Is that all right?"

"All right, Helen, we'll do it right now," consented Alfred. "I will baptize him in a moment. I'll have Jim find the nurse and get me a glass of water," he said as Jim slipped from the room.

Merton returned in a moment with the tumbler of water and was interrupted by a torrent of tears from Helen. "Me, too, Bishop, I've never been baptized."

Chatworthy turned and administered the sacrament to this youngish grandmother. "I baptize thee in the name of the Father and of the Son and of the Holy Ghost . . . O Lord Jesus, help her to know and feel that underneath are the everlasting arms, and that there is no other name under heaven to which she can call for help. Give her a loving sense of Thy near Presence, and fill her with patience, courage, wisdom, and understanding . . . Amen."

He turned and went to the Children's Ward and under the oxygen tent baptized Frankie. Upon Alfred's return he said, "I'm going now, but I'll be back this afternoon. Don't be anxious or fight this thing. It is now completely out of our hands. God's help, and doctor and nursing care will pull the lad out of this." Chatworthy went upstairs to pay a sick call on the Reverend Ralph Goodrich.

As they were visiting, the phone rang; Goodrich picked up the receiver.

"Hey, Reverend," reported the caller, "you can tell Jim Merton that they caught him down at Wagenstern's ranch. Burned him out of a tool shed and the posse shot and killed him."

"Did they find out who it was?"

"Yup. Ed Slater. Tell Jim. Okay? Goodby."

Jim Merton came into the room in a rush. "Did they get him?" he demanded breathlessly.

"It was Ed Slater, Jim," said Goodrich flatly.

"Thought so. He used to go with my little girl some. Always had trouble with him ever since Lou and Frank got married." Jim went on. "He would hang around their place and threaten them. God, he must have been crazy. Never gave 'em a chance. Just blasted away with that damned shotgun at all of 'em, includin' little Frankie. My girl died by the phone as she called me, still holdin' the little fellow in her arms. Poor little guy, he got it too." Jim's huge body was racked with sobs.

In a moment Alfred reached over and slowly and deliberately took the pistol from Merton's pocket. "Let's sit down here on the edge of the bed. Goodrich can move over, he isn't that crippled up," the Bishop said in a low voice. "Now I'm

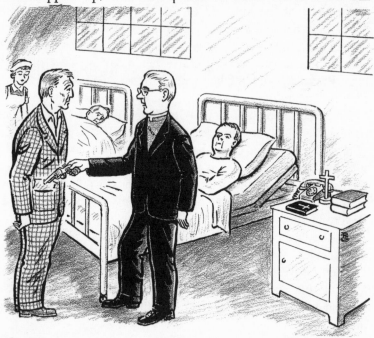

Alfred reached over and slowly and deliberately took the pistol from Merton's pocket.

going to have a prayer with you and it isn't going to hurt anybody and besides you'll feel a lot better."

The Bishop sensed that Jim felt that praying was for old ladies and children, so, without giving him a chance to demur, began, "O Lord, send down Thy strength upon this man. Help him to know that he is not alone in this terrible thing, but that You have been through it, and know what it is to suffer without a just cause . . . The peace of God which passes all understanding, keep your heart and mind in the knowledge and love of God, and of His Son Jesus Christ Our Lord, and the blessing of God Almighty . . . be with you now, and always . . . Amen."

A long, long silence, then Jim spoke slowly and self-consciously, "Bishop, if you got any of that water left you better use it on me, too." So the Bishop baptized Jim, too.

He was about to take his leave of Ralph Goodrich and go over to the Rectory to take Vera Goodrich out to dinner, when Goodrich said, "Wait a minute, Bishop, please."

"Now don't tell me you haven't been baptized," said the Bishop, nearly overcome with emotion.

"Of course, Bishop. But I want to ask you, how do you learn what to do in cases like that? It isn't in the books."

"Listen to the voices, son. Play it by ear. Do what seems necessary to be done without embarrassing or compromising anybody. The Lord can get through, then." Alfred was brusque and impatient. "Now I'm taking your wife out for a decent meal. You stay here and say your prayers."

"—And there'll be a big one included for you, m'lord."

As the Bishop went to bed that night and lay back exhausted on the pillow, the mad events of the day raced through his mind.

"Rest eternal grant unto them O Lord. May they rest in peace . . . and God, what about unloved Eddie Slater?"

125

XII

The Bishop and the Beatnik

THE BISHOP of Blunderland was expected at Horse Meadows, the new suburban development near Clinkerton, to institute the new rector who had recently arrived from the Diocese of Metropole; it was reported that he had done sensational work there with young churchmen on a community-wide basis. Chatworthy had had some doubts about young Ronnie Goodfellow, who was known as "Father Ronnie" since he had graduated from Twinbridge Seminary in the Diocese of Latitude. That he was successful, there was no doubt, so the Bishop had some apprehension, but finally allowed himself to be persuaded to consent to his election by the Vestry of St. Eclampsia's Church. The congregation was made up entirely of families who had moved out near Lost Hole Country Club with their station wagons, Bermuda shorts, and portable rotisseries to live graciously, but casually in the modern manner.

Driving along in silence and reflecting upon the remarkable feeling of good will generated by the Special Convention, he was brought sharply out of his reverie about a job well done, by a sign along the highway screaming at him in its yellow and green nite-lite reflector. Traveling at a high rate of speed, he had time only to note the information:

> St. Eclampsia's the church for you

126

He spotted another suspicious sign down the highway and slowed up to read the message:

> Avoid Disaster!
> See the Pastor!
> Father "Ronnie"
> St. Eclampsia's, Horse Meadows

"Wow!" exclaimed Alfred out loud. "With this as a start, I wonder what to expect when I get to town. Doesn't look good to me. Wonder if there's a committee waiting for me about it."

Another sign at the entrance to Horse Meadows informed the reader, in yellow, green, and red,

> If St. Eclampsia doesn't have it,
> it isn't good for you.

In the rapid succession of signs just inside the city limits, all clamoring for last minute attention, was one of a local furniture house which had the added legend,

> Pray the air-foam way
> Go to St. Eclampsia's Church, Sunday.

The Bishop hunched down in the car seat, secretly hoping that his license number would not identify him until he had had a chance to collect himself. As he turned up Luxuria Drive, he braced himself for come-what-may. Just as he feared, there was a new sign on the corner, to the side of newly painted red church doors. "This sign glows in the dark, too, I'll bet," he said. (And it did, he discovered that evening.) But for the moment he was entranced by the incredibility of the message:

DON'T BE IN THE LURCH, COME TO OUR CHURCH
St. Eclampsia's Episcopal Church
Sunday Services:
8:00 A.M. Begin your risen life with us
9:30 A.M. The family that prays together stays together
11:00 A.M. Don't Change Your Basic Pattern, worship
with us

* * *

FRUNDAY SERVICES
for those who get up too late on Sunday
Fridays at 10:00 P.M.
Father Ronnie Goodfellow, Rector

The Bishop parked his car in the rectory driveway and walked over to the church in a state of shock. He considered himself a tolerant and progressive person, but this was too much. "What will he have done to the inside? These signs may be a warning." Nervously, he jerked the door open and entered. To his surprise, everything was in its usual order except for one thing—a new electronic organ and four folding chairs where the priest's prayer desk used to be. Relieved, he made his way to the undercroft.

Hearing murmurings of young voices, he entered the lower hall quietly to find the Reverend Ronnie Goodfellow standing on his head, and surrounded by fifteen teen-agers sitting cross-

128

"Guess it's a poor way to start **off in** the Diocese, but I'll do better next time."

legged in a circle. No one rose when the Bishop entered, but Father Ronnie quickly dropped to his feet and strode over to the Bishop to introduce himself.

"I'm sorry, Bishop, that my heavy program here made it impossible to attend your Convention. Guess it's a poor way to start off in the Diocese, but I'll do better next time, won't I, gang?"

"Zatz," came the chorus.

"What?" asked the Bishop.

"Zatz," replied Ronnie. "Like 'amen,' man. Gang, this is our Bishop. He's here to cage me tomorrow, like goat me in."

"Zatz."

"Amen," answered Alfred, completely dumbstruck.

Father Ronnie dismissed the gang with a

> Go, cat, go,
> Get hep to the beat from Daddy-o;
> Don't be square, give with nod
> Get cool, church cat,
> Go steady with God.

Alfred weakly made his way to the rectory kitchen, not knowing what to expect in the "pad," as Goodfellow called it. He was agreeably surprised to be met by Father Ronnie's wife, Bonnie. "Seems to be normal and attractive," Alfred estimated, giving a quick look around to see if the living room had any furniture, or just pads. The room seemed normal, too, although he detected a set of bongo drums under the piano.

Later, after a fine dinner prepared by Bonnie, the Bishop finally relaxed. He confessed to himself that he was quite attracted to this young woman, but he was still a bit cautious and restrained with her husband, although Goodfellow gave no further indication of abnormality, or even lack of taste since that disturbing exhibition in the undercroft during the afternoon.

130

THE BISHOP AND THE BEATNIK

"Well, Bishop," Ronnie declared as they rose from the dinner table, "I suppose that we night as well establish ground rules and get our signals straight for tomorrow. I think that I have things pretty well worked out. Now if you will take the eight o'clock service. Good old Blunderland rite is good enough for the early service."

"It's good enough anytime, Goodfellow," defended the Bishop. "Took me ten years to establish a sensible liturgical norm in the Diocese, and it works well."

"Zatz," Ronnie agreed, "but if I may say so, sir, all of it is not relevant to today's generation, hence, I have changed things around at the nine-thirty service. But don't worry about it. I'll take that one and you just sit in the Bishop's chair and give the blessing. The eleven o'clock'll be just the Institution and you run it to suit yourself. Guess that makes us even, doesn't it?"

The Bishop thought that Goodfellow didn't leave much to be settled, but he had to admit to himself that everything was at least planned, which was quite a contrast to many of his visitations.

Having been told that Ronnie was running the Campus Club Dance down at the Antelope Club, Bishop Chatworthy was left to spend the evening with Bonnie. This dance was a weekly affair, he was informed, and was the source of contacts for the choir at the Family Service, and for acolytes, too. The Bishop tried discreetly to approach the subject of parish reaction to this sudden and drastic change. He need not have bothered. Bonnie was right there with the answers.

"Of course, Bishop, some of them are a little concerned about all the activity around here, and Ronnie's unusual method and great talent in working with the teen-agers, but after all, it's their children that he's working with. They called him as Rector to 'do something' with the young people. Then, too, there aren't many old timers around here. They all go to the downtown church," Bonnie explained. It was quite plausible and likely true. Alfred felt better, picked up a copy of *The Episcopalian* magazine and went off to bed.

Morning came. The Bishop celebrated the Holy Communion in a well-filled church—the age-old rite of the breaking of the bread and the blessing of the cup—attended by one acolyte, and afterwards greeted many acquaintances at the church door. No one secretly drew him aside to pass along warning or complaint. Relieved, he returned to the rectory for his breakfast and to gird his loins for the uncertainties that the rest of the morning was to hold for him. Ronnie had just come down the stairs, explaining that he did not get in until two-thirty A.M., and knew that the Bishop wouldn't mind if he were not present at the eight o'clock service.

The Bishop did mind, but he didn't say anything about it, holding his peace, eating his scrambled eggs, and drinking coffee.

"See you in the sacristy at 9:25, Bishop," called out Ronnie as he bounced through the kitchen, binding his cassock and getting the cincture temporarily caught in the door knob.

A little later the Bishop went over to the sacristy, thinking that he had better put on not only the helmet of salvation and the shield of the spirit, but the breastplate of righteousness as well if he were to watch with all perserverance and supplication for all saints at this Family Service. The street was lined with cars, and parents with children were entering the church, already well-filled.

Father Ronnie came into the sacristy as the Bishop was vesting. "Glad to see that you're wearing the red peacock suit instead of the black penguin outfit. Do you have your crocodile suit with you?"

"My *what?*" demanded Alfred.

"Crocodile suit. You know. Cope and mitre. That'd be real cool for the cats, man," explained Ronnie.

"Use the cope and mitre only for Confirmation and Ordination," retorted Alfred impatiently, "This 'peacock suit,' as you call it, will have to do."

"Oh, that's fine. We like to have a bishop around whether he's dressed or not," answered Ronnie.

"You do not," thought Alfred, privately, as he went down to the undercroft and up the stairs to the back of the church. As the narthex doors swung open, he could hear unfamiliar noises coming from the church. "Sounds like a saxaphone and a guitar. Must be someone's car radio left on." It wasn't, he discovered a moment later. The saxaphone and guitar were joined in chorus with the electronic organ, a clarinet, and bongo drums, playing a tune strangely like "O Sion Haste." Father Ronnie stepped up to the Bishop and asked him to wait until all the choirs had processed—he would be specially escorted. Alfred didn't half hear what he said, being already confounded by the bongo beat to "O Sion Haste," as choir number one deserted him and left him standing there, obedient to instructions.

From a side door, near the chancel steps, came another choir wearing red beanies, first coming single file down the side aisle, and, then in two's down the main aisle to the front row of the nave. The hymn stopped. Alfred was still stranded at the entrance when a thunderous roll of snare drums and a chorus of trumpets blared out behind him. He leaped and looked wildly about him. They were there all right, and the congregation was facing the back of the church expectantly, as Alfred composed himself for the anticipated grand entry. "Sounds like 'The Saints Go Marching In.'" He guessed right.

Flanked by two gangling youths, and preceded by a crucifer, two torch bearers, and a chaplain, all wearing burnt orange cassocks and lace cottas, they were off.

Thus, amidst all the noise and splendor, the Bishop was

133

successfully escorted to the Bishop's chair. He smiled as he thought to himself, "If my wife could only see me now, and the good people of St. Lethargus', too!"

The Psalm for the day was dramatically read by a speech choir. The Bishop was a little startled, but approved; it was well done, even by his standards. The Lesson, to his relief, was read from the Phillips translation. It wasn't exactly authorized, but it was much better than he anticipated. So, silent, tacit approval was given for that, too. As he rose for the Canticle, that infernal combo started up. Sounded strangely familiar. His daughter Annie had a 45 r.p.m. record of that tune. What was it? "Teen-Age Love." That's it! What in . . . !

The Beanie Choir broke into the lyrics composed especially for the occasion:

> For someone to talk with,
>   Morning, night, and noon.
> Who doesn't spread secrets
>   You tell 'neath the moon,
> Hand clasped in hand,
> Stroll down the strand.
> Don't make out with a clod—
> Go steady with God.

The Bishop grabbed the arm of the chair for support. Mercifully there was only one verse, but then they swung into a syncopated, versified rendition of the Apostle's Creed. Still stunned, Alfred sank to his knees with the congregation, in supplication to the Almighty, but they didn't have his fervor. Alfred was bracing himself for the Offertory—and well he might. He was surprised to hear the organ begin the familiar tune for "Onward, Christian Soldiers," but he sank back into near coma as the choirs joined together in the new words:

> Onward then ye people,
>   It's all right with God.

Open wide the church doors,
  Give the Lord a nod.
We're the beat through snow and heat,
  We love the Church so odd,
So come on, gang, take the beat,
  Where the saints have trod.
Onward then ye hepcats,
  Play it cool, man, cool,
Church pad for all weirdsmen,
  Be the Lord's footstool.

Chatworthy staggered to his feet and drew up to his height, trying to gather his shaken wits and body into an ordered unit. He brushed past Father Ronnie, crashed into an unwary acolyte, and ascended the steps to the altar. Turning to the congregation, he boomed, "The Lord be with you."

"The sermon, yet, Bishop," stage whispered Goodfellow.

He ignored him, and turned to give the blessing, "The Lord bless you and keep you. . . ."

There was a mixture of "Amens" and "Zatzes." The Bishop strode out to the sacristy in silence. Incoherent with hurt and the display of poor taste, he unvested and went to his room in the rectory to calm down so that he would not say or do anything that he might regret later. He couldn't think of anything to do or say, anyway, in his state.

"Oh, God," he breathed, "what have I done that this should be brought upon me? Maybe someday I will be able to laugh about this whole situation, but right now I need help to keep calm."

Soon Alfred was able to return to the parish hall for the coffee hour, and later, to survive even a blunt and difficult conference with Father Ronnie.

XIII

Miss Platen's Perilous Parlors

MONDAY FORENOON the Bishop dragged into his office, still shaken from his encounter at St. Eclampsia's. He would have to gather strength before going home. Kathleen would hear of it soon enough. He must get there first. But not yet, O Lord, not yet.

"Good morning, Bishop," cheerily called Miss Platen. "I sure admired you at Convention. Everyone did."

The words were like ashes. This woman didn't know yet about the newest crisis in the Diocese. He wandered into his own office and slumped into his chair. Miss Platen came in like a pageant wise man, bearing the mail.

"Not a bit of bad news in the mail," she carolled.

"I don't need mail to get bad news, Penelope," he answered.

"No long distance collect phone calls, either. And the Diocese hasn't been sued for anything all week," she quipped. She stood looking at him. "What's the matter, Bishop? Something wrong?"

"It's just a case of present judgment," he lamented. "I almost hurt my shoulder patting myself on the back for the way Convention was handled. I even began thinking how lucky the Lord is to have me on His side . . . then I spent the week-end at St. Eclampsia's." He shivered. "Tell it not in Gath." He shook. "By the waters of Babylon we sat down and wept . . . Who can sing the Lord's song in a strange land? . . . We hanged our guitars and bongo drums on the trees . . . Oh, Miss Platen, it was dreadful."

"Shall I make an appointment with Dr. Pilldowner?" she suggested brightly.

"No, I'm going home. Should anyone ring, I'll be back in the Spring."

"It *is* Spring, Bishop. Are you sure that you don't want me to call him?"

"Quite. I'll be all right, but I'm either going to can that Junior Grade Moloch or shove him off on the Bishop of Fanfare. He'll get us both murdered in our sleep if I don't stop him."

"What's wrong, Bishop? I haven't seen you like this since Father Dannovich tried to put a cope on the Baptist minister at the community Thanksgiving service at Little Fork five years ago."

"Well, it's in the same league," he answered. "Go steady with God!" he shuddered. " 'Zatz' instead of 'Amen.' " He shuddered again. "I tell you, Miss Platen, it was frightful. It was bizarre. And I was right in the middle of it with that bubble-headed beatnik standing on his head." The Bishop was living it all over again. Miss Platen stood there amazed and puzzled.

"A beatnik priest?" she ventured.

"Not only that, but rector of a parish. Canons or no canons, I'm going to bounce him so high that he'll land on his head and say 'Zatz' . . . And he has such a lovely wife, but I hope to God he won't stay," he added.

The Bishop pulled himself together. "Miss Platen, I will give you the details later; suffice it now to say that I have been through the most horrible experience of my life, blasphemy thrice-confounded, and nobody seemed to be aware of it but me. Pardon me, but I am going home and let the angels minister unto me that I may recover my health." With that, he

137

strode out of the office, leaving Miss Platen standing with pad and pencil.

As he opened the door at home, he heard Kathleen call, "Alfred is that you?"

"Yes, my love," he answered flatly.

"I just heard what you have been through at Horse Meadows," she said consolingly.

"The mocassin telegraph is most efficient," Alfred observed.

"Now don't worry about it, Alfred," she sympathized, trying to be motherly. "Remember you always tell me that the Lord's on your side. Just wait and see."

"After what I was a party to, I'm not sure of it," was his rejoinder.

"A Church Convention and St. Eclampsia's in one week is enough to kill a wise man's camel," she assured him.

"Enough to fell a saint, Kathleen. I would even go to St. Lethargus' as Rector rather than go through that again."

"As you have often said, people like that dig their own graves. Leave it alone for a few days, Alfred, and that man will wind up with a guitar string around his neck."

"That's too merciful an end, unless I can be there to twist the string and hit him over the head with a bongo drum." He smiled at the thought. "All right, I'll forget it until I can calm down . . . Any reason why we can't drive up to Camp Wob-A-Lee for a day or so and see how our new cottage is coming along?"

Wisely, she agreed. (*If I can get him out of here for a while, he'll settle down and deal with this thing sensibly.*)

". . . and a word of greeting to you, dear Miss Platen," announced the Bishop as he entered the sacred halls of the diocesan office, upon his return from the brief visit to Camp Wob-A-Lee.

"Good morning, Bishop," Penelope beamed, "it's nice to

see you in good spirits. There are a thousand things hanging fire, and . . ."

"There always are upon my return to the intellectual and spiritual hub of the Church," observed Alfred. "This is to certify," he went on, "that I came here this morning at the crack of dawn to begin sorting potatoes, and to right many wrongs and do other dramatic and heroic deeds for the kingdom by answering my mail, sending a telegram or two, and making a few long distance phone calls, collect, of course." He made his way to the desk with Miss Platen following him like a bird dog after a wounded goose.

"Now, Bishop," began Miss Platen, as she noticed that he was sizing up the correspondence neatly stacked where he could not avoid seeing it. "There are some matters that need attention first before you get to the mail."

The Bishop reached down into the paper pile and withdrew from the bottom the latest issue of *The Living Church* magazine. "Everything can wait until I learn what the Bishop of Poppyfield is up to. He hasn't made the "Religion" sections of *Time* or *Newsweek* for two months, so something must be brewing." He leafed through the magazine while Miss Platen impatiently waited.

"Ha! I thought so! He's off again!" trumpeted Chatworthy. "We are going to have union with the Revised Covenant Church. So that's where A. Grinfell Popover was when I was in Denver. Scheming with old Faultstaff, the bibbed Bishop of Poppyfield." He read on in silence for a moment. "Listen to this, Penelope: 'The proposed merger would result in the simplifying of clerical dress, for one thing. Although all the clergy would be required to be re-ordained by a committee made up of a military chaplain, a member of the Sons of 1812, and the Mother-of-the-Year, it is expected that the higher the rank achieved in the new church the simpler the garb would be.' "

"How do you like that?" Alfred expostulated. "Following

that to its logical conclusion means that bishops will wear sport coats and bermuda shorts while the laymen wear copes and mitres to church. I'll bet they are planning to corner the vestment market. And won't the laymen be happy!" He paused a moment and then put aside the magazine.

Miss Platen still sat patiently waiting with her pad and pen-

"I'll write him a note." "When?" tartly asked Miss Platen.

cil in readiness as she watched and listened. "Bishop, we simply must get on with things. There is much to be done this morning. Father Shortman called yesterday," she pursued, "and he says that he hasn't received last month's travel check. I made out the check, number A-1871, for $76.41, and mailed it to him two weeks ago. He must be using it for a bookmark."

"Or," suggested the Bishop, "perhaps Mabel got to it first and cashed it. Have you checked with the bank? You know that Shortman is so tight that every time he winks his toes turn up. This is probably the only way that Mabel can buy a new girdle, and I'd be in favor of that." He paused. "I'll write him a note."

"When?" tartly asked Miss Platen.

"After the girdle is paid for, Penelope. Now what else of earth shaking importance do we have to face on this glorious morning?"

"Well, the Executive Council meets next Tuesday, and we will have to go over the agenda, and arrange to bring in chairs from other offices on the floor, and . . ."

Chatworthy cut in with, "We will meet in the Board of Directors room at the Hereford Trust and Savings Bank. Better call Fillmore Bowles and make the arrangements."

"Bishop, we can meet here just as well. All the papers and records and files are at hand. It's much more convenient," she countered.

Alfred turned in his chair. "Miss Platen, I want to have the meeting at the bank. The Council can't make speeches at me so easily in a room like that. I have them at a disadvantage in luxurious surroundings. When we meet here I can't even get them to accept the Treasurer's report. When we meet over there in an atmosphere of six per cent success, then even Alaric Donebetter gets a little euphoric." The Bishop reached for the phone and arranged the matter with Mr. Bowles.

141

"The bank called yesterday to tell you that your travel account is overdrawn," mourned Miss Platen.

"And when is it not?" retorted the Bishop. "Put that item down on the agenda for the Council meeting. Funny thing," he philosophized, "when the clergy run short on travel allowance they lament the hard-heartedness of the Council. When the bishop runs short he complains about the hard-heartedness of those who seek personal relief from him. What's next?"

"You also received a call from the Western Bank that your Discretionary Fund is without sufficient funds," she continued like an apostle of doom.

"I take it that the Discretionary Offerings from the visitations haven't been coming in," pondered Alfred.

"Bishop, you haven't been making any visitations for Confirmation. You have just been meeting with vestries and flying about the whole country and not getting anything done. I mean. . . ." Miss Platen apologetically faltered.

"Guess you are right about the visitations, Penelope, but I am *not* just gadding about the country accomplishing nothing," he answered sharply.

"I didn't mean it that way, really," she explained. "I know what you have to put up with, too." There was a pause. "Oh, I almost forgot the most important thing. There was a call for you this morning just before you came in. It was Miss Kissingham, the parish secretary from St. Nod's Church. She can't find Father Walflauer. He's been missing two days. His car was found by the State Highway Patrol, locked, and parked in a gravel pit outside of town. She said that they suspect violence."

"From Waldo?" questioned the Bishop. "He doesn't have a very high ferocity level. Besides, he has a kind of spearmint sanctity that is invulnerable. Penelope, the chances are that Waldo is over-reacting in trying to preserve his bachelor state. I think that I can find him." He reached for the telephone and called the ranger's office at Mellowstone Park. In a moment he was talking to the Reverend Waldo Walflauer who explained that he had met the park ranger on the highway, parked his car, and gone on into the park with him for a couple of days.

"See?" said Alfred, as he hung up the phone, "good old Waldo was just escaping from the Harvest Home Bazaar. I told him to stay a week if he wanted to."

"Well, you'd think he'd let them know . . ."

"Why don't you call Miss Kissingham and put her on his trail?" As an afterthought, "and have her call off the police."

"Bishop," hesitated Miss Platen, "there is a letter here that I didn't place on your desk. It's about that dreadful old jalopy that you drive around the country. Some of our people are embarrassed by it and want to know if you really plan to get rid of it soon."

There was a brief silence. "Let me see that letter." He read the note. "All right, I'll answer it right now." The Bishop dropped the letter into the wastebasket, leaned back in his chair, and began dictating.

"Dear Mrs. Sitwell: In answer to your worried note, may I reply by stating the three requirements necessary for a man to function as a Bishop of Blunderland? First, he must have a sense of humor; secondly he should be unhappily married, because he is so frequently absent from home for long periods of time; and thirdly he requires a private income. I am sadly lacking in the latter two and, according to others, over-endowed with the first. With every good wish to you, I remain, Faithfully yours, and still driving the Eocene 6."

"Do you really want to say that?" Penelope cautiously questioned him.

"I do," pontificated Chatworthy. "And here's another letter in answer to the Bishop of Aphasia.

"Dear Harold: In answer to your query concerning the

143

Reverend P. E. Cusa of the Diocese of Blunderland, I can certify that he has served to his own complete satisfaction for the last three years, and that if you are considering giving him a berth, be sure and make it a wide one. Faithfully yours."

"Bishop, you will never get a place for Mr. Cusa if you don't write a more encouraging letter than that," remonstrated Miss Platen.

"But Harold is a good friend of mine, Penelope," defended Alfred. "I am saving Cusa for a certain other bishop—when he has had time enough to forget that he palmed off an undesirable on the Diocese of Aphasia when Harold wasn't looking."

"Well, if you ask me," volunteered Miss Platen, "I think that it is a shame that the Church doesn't have a clergy placement system. Sometimes I hold my breath hoping that you won't fall into the trap of sweet words that some of your brother bishops set up for you in their attempt to rid themselves of a clerical problem. I don't think that any of you trust each other." With that judgment made, Miss Platen posed her pencil and dutifully awaited dictation.

Ignoring her readiness to get on with the work, Chatworthy leaned back in his chair comfortably. "Now, Penelope, most of the bishops are fair with each other. In any case, one soon learns whom he can trust. Admittedly, some of them fancy themselves to be horse traders, but as I go about the country and see their stables I am convinced that they come off the worse for their delusions. The Lord, in His infinite wisdom and mercy has spread out these inadequate and unfortunate men among us so that each of the bishops have a few. It's only on very bad days that we suspect that we have more than our share."

The Bishop remembered that he hadn't answered her statement, so he turned back to that matter in a last attempt to avoid the morning mail. "A clergy placement system is still only a possibility in the dim future, Penelope. Among the reasons for our unwillingness as a Church to face up to the need is that, like the rest of our social order, we actually *like* our present ecclesiastical structure based on status, prestige, and power. In the Church, if one plays it right, one can go from log cabin to White House, so to speak, or from curate's apartment to bishop's palace. They like it this way, especially those whose positions as cardinal rectors have made them secure and unassailable, as long as they keep their noses clean, that is. It's a sort of clerical adaptation of Darwin's theory of the survival of the fittest, except that the Church's jungle is made of stained glass."

"That's all most interesting," said Miss Platen, "but I think that you are making excuses."

"Oh, is that so?" the Bishop shot back, straightening up in his chair. "All right. Take a look at this great Diocese. Who pays the bills and, therefore, who calls the dances? The cardinal rectors, of course. In our case they are, without exception, highly competent men. Oh, I don't see eye to eye with them on certain matters, nor they with me. We do indulge in a certain amount of game-playing, and they love to engage me in brinkmanship, but they did emerge from the crowd because of their gifts and abilities."

Miss Platen was wearying of his lecture and turned him back to his letters. At that moment the Bishop's friend, Bert Boswell, appeared in the doorway. Chatworthy accepted this providential rescue and invited Father Boswell to go out for coffee because there were some matters that he wished to discuss with him about the Diocesan Council meeting that afternoon. Successfully escaping his secretary-captor Chatworthy gave her a semi-fiendish smile as he turned to go out the door. "Carry on, Miss Platen, but not too much. Remember, the Council is watching. Farewell."

XIV

How to Budget a Balance

AS THE ELECTRONIC carillon rang out on the crisp morning air the homey tune, "Work, for the Night is Coming," Alfred observed that the Vice-President in charge of chimes was on the job and showing his usual lack of good musical taste.

"Good morning, Bishop Chatworthy," called out a feminine voice, from behind him as he opened the door to the Hereford Trust and Savings Bank, where the Council meeting was to be held. "You passed right by without looking at me," chided the well-furnished Scheherezade Winkbetter, as she spiked her way along the terrazzo floor to the near presence of the Bishop.

"Sherry," replied Alfred, with a twinkle in his eyes, and a gentlemanly smile, "if I *had* looked at you, I could not have passed you by. I must exchange the brighter prospects of your company for the sober legislation of the Council this morning. Through the kindness of your brother, Fillmore, we are to behave like bankers today."

"You can say the nicest things. You know that you're my favorite Bishop."

"I also happen to know, Sherry, that I am the only bishop you are acquainted with. Futhermore, flattery is like shaving lotion. Smell it, but don't swallow it."

"Now Bishop, just remember that you're the one that started it," laughed Sherry as she headed for Fillmore's office.

146

"*You can say the nicest things. You know that you're my favorite Bishop.*"

Alfred went up to the second floor where he joined the group of early arrivals and had a handshake all around. Bert Boswell motioned for him to draw aside.

"Alfred, I forgot to tell you that I drove in with Stanley Perse this morning. Like most treasurers, he sings in a minor key, but today I think he's got something special on his mind," said Bert in a low voice.

"Why? Did he intimate anything?"

"No, but as we drove along I said, 'Stanley, look at that band of sheep. They have just been sheared.' He answered by saying, 'Yeah, on this side, anyway.' He didn't have much else to say all the way, and if he has an attitude like that I think you ought to be on guard," concluded Boswell.

"Thanks, Bert." The Bishop drifted off for a conference with John Hillman.

In a few minutes everyone had arrived, and after an opening prayer, they all settled down to the business at hand. Soon, the Bishop called for the Treasurer's report.

Stanley Perse passed out the financial statements and began to read each item of the five page report in droning detail.

"Mr. Perse," interrupted the Bishop, "I believe that, if you will move its acceptance and then permit the Council to ask questions, much valuable time may be saved for all of us." He smiled and recognized John Hillman.

"I second the motion and call for the question," moved Hillman.

Before Stanley knew what had happened, the smoke had all cleared away. "Are you sure that there aren't any questions, gentlemen? After all, we have spent a lot of money." Perse was disappointed.

Harry Rosewell spoke up. "As far as I am concerned, Stanley, you have given an excellent account of your stewardship and I want to express my thanks. I have some questions. They aren't on what we have spent, but just where do we stand now?"

Stanley Perse brightened a bit, tightened up his lips so that the pressing little wrinkles showed all around, and picked up with renewed hope. "Well, now," he announced, clearing his throat, "the Assessments and Apportionments are all paid up to November first except for St. Lethargus' and St. Laodicea's at Luke Springs, and that's real good. But there are still six weeks to go before the end of the year and I can't see where we are going to get another nickel."

"Why not?" demanded Father Derringer.

"Are you implying that Grace Church won't be paying our two thousand balance by December?" challenged Sewickley Codger.

"I don't mean that at all," defended Stanley, "but money has been coming in so well that these places must be paying us first instead of other obligations and it'll catch up with them next month. Something is bound to happen."

"I move that all vicars' salaries be cut 10%," said Alaric Donebetter, sensing imminent disaster, to whom cutting back costs was a way of life.

"May I speak, sir?" asked the Reverend Gerald Swemp of Trinity, Clinkerton, addressing the Bishop.

"The floor is yours," permitted the Bishop.

"As you all know, the lumber mill will be closing down for a six-week period, and this may affect us temporarily, but I fail to share Mr. Perse's concern," said Swemp encouragingly.

"Say, Stanley," interrupted Gib Morland, "are you worried about the cattle market."

"I think we should be," replied Stanley, somewhat encouraged that his shipment of doom might finally be unloaded.

"Well, now, Stanley," Morland went on, "every three or four years all the doctors and schoolteachers, and you merchants, too," he added, pointing to him, "buy a few head of cattle and go into competition with us full time operators. This raises the cattle population about fifteen million head and that knocks the price down. And what's happening? Yeah, you're losing your investment. It's your own danged fault. We are just out to separate the men from the boys in the cattle business and you are spreading your personal doom over the whole economy and that of the Diocese and it isn't going to change it one bit." He crushed his cigar in the ash tray and mumbled something about skeletons at a feast.

After a brief but deathlike silence, the meeting proceeded through the agenda. From his seat as Chairman the Bishop felt that he was looking through a hole bored into the economic and social structure of the land. Morland had stopped his mumbling and was back in control by the time that the Council had gone into the subject of clergy housing. "You know," volunteered Gib, "I got a man working for me down on the ranch and sometimes I don't pay him regular, so in fun we have a big deal. He says that he'll work free for five years and then he will get the ranch. Then I can work for him for five years and get it back." A relieved laugh went up all around.

John Hillman spoke up, "Gentlemen, the Diocese should set an example of decent living by providing good homes for the clergy. These men and their wives have to live and work in some one else's house; and they cannot own their own, so we ought to provide the best housing we can."

The Bishop added, "And that is just what is going on, and what I want to see increase, because then it is easier to keep men on the job when their wives are happy in a good house." Then, as an afterthought, he said, "Some congregations have splendid rectories for their priests, and in other places they have splendid priests for their rectories."

"There is another matter of old business," announced Harry Rosewell, the secretary. "I have a note here from the Reverend Robert Shortman that he does not have enough travel money to go through November and December." Harry waited for an answer.

Boswell finally spoke up, "I move that the secretary type

out the parable of the wise and foolish virgins and send it to him along with the check for $76.41 that he asks for." (*Uproarious laughter.*) Moved and seconded.

As the final business for the day the Bishop announced the appointment of the Nominating Committee for the next Diocesan Convention, to be held in May at St. Eclampsia's, Horse Meadows.

"Are we supposed to bring our own guitars and bongo drums, Bishop?" Sewickley Codger slily asked.

The Bishop smiled. "By then I think I'll have a job for him as a Coffee House chaplain in Greenwich Village. He can work part time up at Heaven-on-the-Hudson," he replied, getting into the spirit of the waning moments of a long day.

Alfred was about to dismiss the meeting when Stanley Perse, the Treasurer of the Diocese, cleared his throat and asked for the floor. "Now, Bishop, I don't want to be misunderstood, because this isn't personal, but several people have told me that there ought to be an audit of the Discretionary Fund. I said that I would bring the matter up before the Council."

The Bishop could feel his blood pressure rising. "Stanley," he said slowly, "there is no endowment fund in the Diocese whose income may be used for discretionary purposes. Any Discretionary Funds which I *do* have, I raise myself, and I might add, for the education of busybodies, that the demands on that Fund exceed six thousand dollars a year. When the money is forthcoming from Diocesan Funds I might contrive a report. Frankly, however, a discretionary fund is, by definition, one which is left solely in the hands of the administrator and, therefore, it is nobody's business. Tell them that, too," Chatworthy added.

Collecting himself after that pronouncement, he scanned the room for other attackers. Clifford Pokemore, who had been silent all day, raised his hand to speak. (Mr. Pokemore was terrified by a new idea, and was the sort of person who always agreed with the last individual that he talked to).

Imitating the unfortunate Mr. Perse, Clifford, with his genius for mal-timing, said, "Bishop, there is nothing personal in this but there *is* some complaint about your being absent from the Diocese for long periods of time, and that as long as you are being paid by the Diocese, naturally people think that you should be here except when necessary to leave." Mr. Pokemore lit the wrong firecracker that time.

There was an ominous silence. Chatworthy slowly rose to his feet and began pacing back and forth across the room. "Mr. Pokemore," he said in a barely controlled and quiet voice," Just where do you think that I get the money for discretionary use, out of a hat? Gentlemen, when the Diocese acknowledges and assumes all of its responsibilities, then, I'll stay home. Council adjourned."

The Council members filed out in silence. Boswell waited around so that he could help calm down his friend, who by now, was as angry as a turkey in a duck pond. Finally he spoke, "Alfred, let's go up to the Club and have a drink. After a day like this I don't think that you ought to put food on an empty stomach."

Alfred smiled and looked up from the table where he was busy gathering up papers in smouldering silence. "You know, Boswell, a bishop needs four mitres: one to wear, one to talk through, one to pass for donations, and another one to pull rabbits out of. Come on let's go."

XV

The Mystic Bishop of Blunderland

THE BISHOP of Blunderland had arisen early on Sunday and had driven over eighty miles to Luke Springs to conduct services for them at St. Laodicea's, the Vicar having been invited to the College of Preachers for a week. It did not improve the Bishop's spirits when he arrived to find the church locked and a note tacked to the door announcing that there would be services at 11:00 A.M. It was not 7:30 A.M. As he turned to walk down the steps, planning to ease his anger by breakfast at leisure, Alfred broke into dialogue with himself.

"Now, see here, Chatworthy, you're always talking about taking time to pray. You'll never have a better opportunity."

"After breakfast," urged Alfred the man. "You have nearly three hours on your hands."

"The first part of the day, at least, belongs to the Lord," answered the Bishop, as he went around to the side of the church and let himself in through an unlocked basement window. He went up the stairs, into the sanctuary, and sat in the Bishop's chair.

"This is the worst place a man can meditate," thought Alfred. He got up and went to the back of the church and knelt down in the last pew. No use. Prayers would not come.

"Of course they won't," reminded Alfred the man. "You've had a week of it, Convention, Goodfellow, and Council. You're tired and sleepy. Out of practice."

153

The Bishop let himself in through an unlocked basement window.

"All the time excuses," thought the Bishop, as he spiritually glared at Alfred the man. "In any event, I am going to sit back and try to smooth out a few wrinkles and try to push back the crowded thoughts, events, and crises that make me so blasted angry." The Bishop sat quietly for a few moments and reflected that this old building did have a spiritual climate to it. It had not occurred to him on his countless visits to St. Laodicea's Church that anybody had ever prayed in it. He smiled to himself. "Guess I never noticed that there ever had been any praying around here. They have always been a discontented lot. Apparently some of them got over it, though."

The roof heaved and sighed as the wind smoothed down the shingles. The doors, the windows, the whole building seemed to be breathing. The windows of the saints looked down upon an (almost) empty church, casting their warm colors upon the gray walls and the nicked and weathered homemade pews. Vacantly, Alfred watched a boxelder bug wearily and uncertainly hitch his way across the flat red desert of carpet, waving his antenna about with the forlorn hope that he may be coming to the end of his journey. Everything seemed to be waiting for end of the long week and the proclaiming of another little Easter.

The noise and clamor inside the Bishop was now subsiding. He began to sense that there was something going on in the church that his own inner dialogue of self-pity and self-interest had kept him from hearing. Apparently he had arrived in the midst of a conversation.

"I wish you wouldn't stand there glaring so," complained the Pulpit as he addressed the new stained glass Window.

"Can I help it because I was installed on the north side and catch the glare off the white rectory? It's hard on me, too. I'm just a wreck after a sunny day. Please, have patience with me; I will repay you all when I have weathered a bit," defended the Window.

"After all," creaked the Pews, addressing the Pulpit, "you aren't so venerable yourself. We've been here since the church was built. We were put together by that strab-eyed carpenter; one eye on the nail and the other on the Cross, so to speak. If we do say so ourselves, we carry quite a bit of weight around here. Dear Pulpit, you have it easy. You get pounded only once a week, especially when the Vicar tries to emphasize weak points in his sermon, though I'll admit there have been plenty of them."

"That reminds me," announced the Lectern, rustling his pages, "remember the day the Bishop was late for Evening Prayer? He raced clear through the Psalm for the fifteenth day and on into the Old Testament Lesson before he got his second wind. Then he concluded with, 'Here endeth the First Inning.' Chatworthy gave himself away on that one. He had been listening to the World Series on his car radio all the way over."

"Now to get back to the point," interrupted the windowed Lady in Blue, "I don't see where any of you have any cause for complaint. Now take me for instance. . . ." The Lectern turned off his reading light, smoothed down his eagle feathers, and stood at ease. The Lady glared at him and continued, "Once I had the place of honor up alongside the Altar, on the Gospel side. Then last summer, when my arm was broken during a hailstorm, the arm that holds the lily, you know, and I had an eye knocked out, I was taken down and repaired. You have no idea what I went through, riding in the back seat of that station wagon all the way to Denver, wrapped in an old blanket! Well, anyway, who goes up in my place when I'm away? St. Paul, that's who. Upon my return, I was put back in this obscure corner in the Nave, right where Mr. Squatwell always sits. And after all those years up with the clergy!"

"You know why you were moved, don't you?" boomed out the Diapason. "You have never approved of a single priest that we have had here since 1902. I have heard many of them say to the organist that your stony gaze and raised eyebrow completely unnerved them. No wonder we have such a turn-over of rectors. We weren't surprised that you were moved back to the rear of the church."

Weakly defending herself, the Lady in Blue replied, "After all, I'm an Altar Guild Window. It says so right on the glass."

"Come, brethren, can we not dwell together in unity?" trumpeted the Flag, waving his stripes.

"I have something to say about that," spoke the Lectern as he fixed a glassy stare on the vocative Window. 'At the same time, came the disciples unto Jesus, saying, 'Who is the greatest in the kingdom of heaven?' Eighteenth chapter of St. Matthew, first verse," he added, adjusting the markers.

"And, dear Lectern, the Scripture continues, if you will look farther on, 'Except ye be converted, and become as little children, ye shall not enter into the kingdom of heaven,' " called out the Font, the Ewer snapping his lid in applause.

"Why don't you ask the Altar Cross what he thinks," suggested the Choir Pews. "We're gummed up enough as it is, without all this disputation. Would anyone like a cough drop? The altos left a half a box of them here last Sunday."

"Maybe they're left over because it's within the octave of St. Blasius," commented the Missal.

"I've been on the Altar many years," said the Cross, "and have witnessed many things. As an example, take the Bishop sitting over there. He's doing just about the same as everyone else who comes in here at odd hours. He just sits there and looks up at the Rood and me and at the Tabernacle. I think he believes what he teaches and tries to practice what he preaches, and he still finds warfare all the time, even early in the morning. . . ."

"When our song shall rise to Thee," interjected a Hymn Book.

"I wish someone would change my numbers more often,"

complained the Hymnboard. "Same old ones all the time. And they stay up all week. I never look nice or wear anything new."

"The hairs of your head are all numbered," rumbled the Lectern, his markers trembling.

"Dearly beloved brethren," began the Prayer Desk, "the Scripture moveth us in sundry places, to acknowledge and confess our manifold sins and wickedness."

"Does it really?" inquired the Altar Rail. "They may be sinners but this parish isn't miserable."

"It says here," broke in the Prayer Desk, "that there is no health in us."

"That may be true, but do the people think so?" asked the Alms Bason. "I don't see much change. A hundred different priests have knelt here down through the years. What do you suppose they thought about the people and their religion?"

"Much the same as we do, probably," replied the Credence Table. "Some of them come half-heartedly, expecting a hand-out of power."

"I'll give credence to that, Table," replied the Altar, who was feeling very fine because of the new oriental rug in front of him. "They knew all too well how the forces of evil. . . ."

"Sh! The Gargoyle on the door might hear."

". . . work within the human soul. I see many persons who come and kneel beside my friend, Altar Rail, who are trying to recover. A few want to be freed of consequences so that they can go on sinning. You know, 'the Devil when sick a saint would be' sort of thing. But there are more who know they have a broken heart and come to the foot of Calvary to be made whole."

"I carry as great a weight around here as the Pews, but in a different sense," agreed the Altar Rail, "and I might add, that few as they are, there are always some who swing on the gate of Eternal Life, so to speak."

"Of course," spoke up the Kneelers, "there are some who

are here occasionally for selfish reasons, believing that they may be externally improved, or get what they think they want, or need. Sort of like trying to change God's mind. These people aren't much of a burden to us, for they don't use their knees. They lean on brother Pew."

"Spiritual millstones, so to speak," replied the Pulpit, waving his antependia.

"We don't need to be so critical," said the Altar Cross. "The crux of the matter is that this building is being prayed in. We don't *all* have smoke in our eyes," glancing sidewise at the Censer. "Every day someone finds out that he is a loved person, at least by the One who is here with us all the time, day and night."

"Look at our silent friend," chimed the Sanctus Bell. "He's standing up now. He seems to be straighter than when he came in."

"I'll wager he gives the residue of the Church something to think about during the sermon this morning," prophesied the Font.

"Oh, me!" moaned the Pulpit. "Even though he is a Bishop in the Church of God, I should think he'd lose his faith."

"What!! And leave the Church?" spoke up the Lady in Blue.

"No!" thundered the Pulpit. "I said lose his faith NOT lose his mind!"

"The Lord be with you," invited the Prayer Desk.

"With *us?*"

"Why not? We can glorify God, too, by just being ourselves. It says so right on this Brass Plate."

As the Bishop of Blunderland unlocked the church door from the inside and started for the Daisy Cafe, he thought, "Perhaps I should have a cup of coffee and an egg or two before the service. I feel a bit unsettled. No wonder there are so few mystics, if they have to survive ecstasies of fantasy like this before a more pious experience occurs."

XVI

You Can't Go Home Again?

THE FOUR FRIENDS of many years met for their quiet reunion at the appointed hour in the Oak Room of the Plaza Hotel and filled the air with light talk all through the dinner and their cigars. Alfred had his friends weak from laughter at his account of the Ronnie Goodfellow fiasco at Horse Meadows.

Jim Sayers broke in, "Being a bishop today is a thankless job. I've got enough grief handling a big parish. The thought of multiplying that by sixty or so places turns me to jelly."

"Looks like you're safe from being a bishop, Jim," remarked George Orian. "You've been nominated so many times that everybody is suspicious of you."

"And they should be," rejoined Ad Beamer. "They're afraid that as soon as you got in you'd be singing another tune." Beamer had voluntarily relinquished his Orders fifteen years prior, largely, Alfred felt, because of his monumental impatience with both laymen and clergy, including bishops. Ad now worked for a public relations firm. "The clergy haven't changed much since my day, with exceptions so rare that they are regarded as eccentrics; and this includes you, Sayers," he added. "Successful ministers of the Gospel are insecure and intimidated men. They advance only as they placate, appease, bamboozle, and manipulate the demanding elements in a parish."

"You're talking about the man I love, meaning me," answered Alfred with a smile.

"As for you, Chatworthy," said Beamer, as he faced his friend directly, "you are one of the few men I have ever known who could let the devil go into a revolving door first, and come out ahead of him."

George Orian spoke. "That's why I left the parochial ministry for chaplaincy work in the hospital. I wouldn't endure what Sayers and His Lordship have to put up with."

"It isn't so bad as all that, George," replied Sayers. "I've got

"You are one of the few men I have ever known who could let the devil go into a revolving door first, and come out ahead of him."

it all worked out. In a Church like ours, where we haven't settled the Reformation yet, parish calling is the big deal. I have it operating on a smooth system. Every Monday morning I find out from the parish treasurer which individuals are delinquent in their pledges and then assign the curates and the parish caller to visit them during the week. The idea, of course, is that most of these will be in church the following Sunday, clutching their paid-up pledges in their tight fists. A call every three months takes care of these dreary matters. As long as the bills are paid and the budget money keeps coming in, then I'm free to preach as I judge best. I also have a deal with the ambulance people, and the girls at the front desks in the hospitals. I'm usually there before the patient, or one of my staff is. One can also cultivate the local bier barons so that you can keep abreast of who's dying at home. If you take care of those matters, the people leave you alone," he concluded.

"All hail, the modern pastor speaketh," sneered Beamer. "You, who always throw a curve at the Madison Avenue boys. Jim, I'm ashamed of you."

"What am I to do, Ad?" asked Jim Sayers. "You just make yourself miserable and ineffective if you don't take steps to shut out the noise of strangers in the house of God. Everyone wants the Church to bless what he does, from the service club luncheon to the community betterment meeting called to protect real estate values. I am always being imposed ·upon to bless self-interest. If I didn't build a wall around my priesthood, and leave only a door open for the broken-hearted, my whole ministry would be destroyed. Instead of being allowed freely to feed the sheep, I am gradually compelled to entertain the goats. You would still be a priest, Ad, only you couldn't find a way out as I did. I do what I do so that I can function as a priest. I expose my curates to them so that they may learn by experience that there is more than one use for an altar rail."

"And what might that be?" inquired Alfred.

162

"To separate the clergy and laity, dear Bishop," explained Jim hastily. "The clergy have the greater function on one side and the laymen on the other. Only today nobody seems to be happy unless he is on the other side of that for which he is called. I take care of everything on one side and let the layman take care of everything on the other, and use this 'calling' nonsense to keep everybody happy."

"There is a profound disarrangement of function in the Church," commented George. "I suppose that's what drove me into hospital work. The arrangement today is like a chocolate sundae. The laymen represent the ice cream, marbleized by vestries, guilds, organizations, and committees. The syrup is the clergy, and the pretty cherry on the top is the Bishop. The system, as it now operates, could easily dispense with bishops entirely—an idea which has often been considered in secret hearts." He smiled at Alfred.

"Go on, reverend sir, dear father and chaplain," urged Chatworthy. "I think you've got hold of something."

Orian was pleased. He cleared his throat, nodded to his contemporaries and made a mock bow to Alfred. "It is well to remember that the Church's Constitution and Canons were written by men who, I suspect, for the most part, didn't think that the Church would long survive in America anyway. It was too much like the Established Church and identified with monarchy. The major interest of those men was to avoid giving offense to non-churchmen. They wanted bishops in name only, pious and sweet old gentlemen who were rectors of large parishes, or presidents of small colleges, who would be available for confirmations, ordinations, and the laying of cornerstones, as well as praying over political conventions. When they were not so engaged they could stay home and develop a reputation for piety, humility, and learning, and leave the running of the Church to the clergy and laity."

"The man's eloquent," exclaimed Sayers.

163

"A godly and well-learned man, too, just like his Bishop," needled Ad.

"Go on, George. I want to hear more," urged Alfred.

"As I was saying, as the crash of applause required me to pause," he bowed, smiling at his own rhyme, "there hasn't been much change in this arrangement since. The laymen happily discovered that bishops provided inexpensive office help and could do the work of five employees and confirm at the same time. They were also handy to play the role of scapegoat when things went awry. There was, in that person, one who could be blamed for the monstrous errors of crowd thinking and group-committee decisions. So today we have the astounding spectacle of watching the cat telling the dog how to bark."

"Excellent, excellent!" applauded Alfred. "That reminds me of our Special Convention a while back. One of the clergy-sponsored resolutions was that the Bishop should be a father-in-God. One priest arose to amend the motion to read 'Grand-father in God.' I think that's what they really meant, too. My clergy are strong on the authority of the Church and the Bishop, as long as they aren't on that end of the whip that stings."

"I can see it from both sides of the fence," said Ad, the PR man. "From my desk I can see the same attitude in secular life. As a people we insist upon God's benevolence. Every-where we find signs of His favor and approval, namely, pros-perity. Doesn't this show that the people are right? We don't need authority, now. We don't like it anyway, so we reduce the idea of omnipotence into respect for law and order, pro-viding that it coincides with whatever we happen to be plot-ting. We are an easy going people, my friends, and careless about everything except business ventures, and we have come to believe that God is that way, too. We've made ourselves believe that occasional and sporadic worship is enough, as long as it coincides with national festivals and paganized religious feasts. We try to convince ourselves that God is vitally concerned over our trivial activities and that He is unconcerned with sex, religion, economics, and politics, mainly because of His confidence that we can handle those disagreeable matters in our own way. God is invited to write editorials, through His clergy of course, on the vagaries of society in direct proportion to their remoteness. His works are rumored abroad by the religious editors on Saturday and again on Monday: God makes the papers twice a week in our culture. Clergymen are called movers and shapers of the nation, yet they are all busy explaining away the devil, ignoring sin, and looking for things to get even better."

"Ad's steak was too rare," observed Sayers.

"Don't be too hard on the man because he has done some thinking," defended George. "I'll admit that he does annoy me by throwing rocks from the indefensible position he is in as an ex-priest."

"Now, look Sayers," pursued Ad, "take a good look at the picture. The churches aren't different, they're all tossed salads, looking and tasting alike; they aren't inharmonious, they have a conflict of purpose; membership is inherited, not decided upon, and it is all dictated by geography, personal social requirements, and economic identification for the sake of expediency." Ad paused for a moment, still under full steam. "My pious brethen, I give you the Church: embraced without commitment, changed without spiritual conflict, and deserted without pain. I give you the Church: self-conscious in worship, self-righteous in judgment, and self-concerned with economic survival. I give you the Church: miracles renounced, the Lion of Judah tamed, and her bishops always agreeable. Where is the Virgin Mary? If she's around at all, she has become a smiling young mother! Where is John the Baptist? He's become the playmate of the boy, Jesus! Where is the Godman? He's become an innocent victim in a great betrayal!"

"The Church lost a preacher and a prophet when Beamer defected," said Sayers. "I wish you could say that from my pulpit—sometime when I am a thousand miles away."

"Twenty-five years ago," continued Beamer persistently, "I stood before the altar in my new white vestments. I raised my hand in blessing over the congregation. Within six months they welled up before me and rolled over me and crushed the love of man right out of me. I consoled myself that the seed had been planted, and that they were too late and could not prevail. But do you know what they were doing? They were meeting in the back room of a downtown store drafting a letter to the bishop demanding a rector who would be more considerate of the selfish desires of the people. And now hear the voice of the Church from the board of director's room at the bank with three and one half per cent on savings; what do they care if the Church declines and becomes tamer as long as they have their pew, their gentleman god, and a subservient clergy to deliver weary homilies to benumb the occasional seeker after the Holy One? And I stood on the rectory porch guiding the moving van to the door and hoping for a letter from the Bishop—a letter that never came—Hey waiter, bring us another round."

There was a long silence after Ad Beamer's penetrating and extensive tirade. The first to speak was Alfred. "Ad, was there anything in the Ordination vows that would make you understand that you were to be immune from spiritual suffering? What about Moses, Aaron, Eli? What about Isaiah, Amos, Jeremiah? You talked like the prophets tonight, but only to your friends. There wasn't any suffering in sounding off to us, was there?" The Bishop paused. No one felt like saying anything. He continued. "What about your Lord? The Apostles? The saints? The martyrs? George and Jim, and myself, and a countless host of others? It's never been any different, Ad. You make it sound as though it never happened to anyone but you. Our Lord hasn't spared any of His priests yet . . ."

George Orian spoke first. "Every priest, at some time or other, having put his hand to the plow, turns and looks back, sometimes because he doesn't like the terrain ahead. You're *still* being dragged along because you're all tangled up in the harness. Wise up, O Man of God!"

"Why don't we talk about the Republicans, or something," suggested Ad, who had been visibly shaken by his diatribe.

"It's nearly midnight," announced Alfred. "Time to knock it off, anyway."

The turn which the evening had taken made each man desire to be alone, so, without much fussing, the bill was paid, they bade each other goodnight, and went off into the night. Ad Beamer looked like a combination of Peter and Nicodemus as he sped unblessed, into the neon glare of Broadway.

"Is it going to be one of *those* nights?" the Bishop asked himself as he made ready for bed. He lay in bed a long time, eyes open in the darkness. He could feel the one-three thump of the danceband feeling its way along the walls, invading every room and every floor. He got up and smoked a cigarette and stood at the window looking down on what looked for all the world like C. S. Lewis's "gray town," and felt like a character out of a Charles William's novel.

"The trouble is," thought the Bishop back in bed again, "most of what Ad said is so." Alfred rolled over on to his back again. "I am responsible for twelve thousand of God's children, but they cannot listen, they can only hear. They cannot eat, yet they starve." He thought back to Harry Rosewell at St. Laodicea's, Luke Springs. "There's Harry, right out of *Main Street,* content with his dull life, dull family, dull business. He thinks he's happy with his dull ideas, dull virtues, and dull vices. He enjoys neither goodness nor wickedness, but swings suspended between the two, and, worst of all, doesn't even know it. He repeats the platitudes of service clubs, puts his hand over his heart every Monday at noon, and believes in party platforms. I probably have thousands like him who are

167

totally dedicated to mediocrity by choice, including a dull home, dull work, and I even think, a dull church . . . My Lord, you went through it; what do we do now?"

The Bishop *was* tired. He could think no more. He drifted momentarily into the no-man's land through which everybody goes before he is blessed with a deeper sleep. The telephone rang. He jerked as if he had received an electric shock. He reached over to the table.

"Yes?" he muttered.

"Alfred? This is Ad." A silence punctuated only by Beaman's tortured breathing. "I'm sorry, Bishop, but I have something that I have to ask you. Would you really take back a man who had turned from the plow and got tangled up in the harness?"

Alfred lightened as he thought, "The Lord works fast, once He sets his mind to it." He answered his friend. "I'll have breakfast with you, Ad. I'm glad you called. Now we can both get some sleep. I think that this is the way our Lord wants it, so we'll try to work it out in the morning." Alfred hung up, filled with a new warmth and quiet. As he dropped off to sleep he thought, "When will I ever learn that when He tells me to jump, all I have to do is jump. . . ."

XVII

Wise Up, O Men of God

NOW THAT "Father Ronnie" Goodfellow, and his wife Bonnie, had left St. Eclampsia's, Horse Meadows, in favor of the position of Director of Youth Program in the Diocese of Euphoria, Alfred Chatworthy felt much more relaxed over the prospects of having the Diocesan Convention there.

Feeling that all was in readiness for the witness of the Church in Horse Meadows, and fortified by the presence of his good wife Kathleen, the Bishop arrived in Clinkerton, registered at the Snoozemore Hotel, and drove on out to St. Eclampsia's, in the Horse Meadows suburbs.

Chatworthy found, to his satisfaction, that Father Swemp and Bert Boswell had already arrived and were explaining the mysteries of a Chatworthy convention to the recently inducted rector. The Bishop was smugly pleased with his "catch," for he had stolen him from St. Stanstill's, Headlong City, right out from under the nose of the Bishop of Caseharden.

Bert drew the Bishop aside and said, "Alfred, can't we do without the trumpet trio and the tympani for tonight? That's pretty extreme business in this country. I think that the reaction would be bad, and just add to our problems."

"Now, Bert," consoled Chatworthy, "I owe it to the good people of St. Eclampsia's to give them some good music. The last time that I was here I was serenaded by guitar and bongo drums. It will drown Goodfellow out of memory. Besides I like a big drum rumble and trumpet fanfare to get things off to a good start."

169

"I don't know why I always try to protect you," lamented Boswell.

"The blaring entrance and procession will take second place to the Bishop's Charge, anyway, Boswell, so there's no use getting apprehensive over the accompaniment. Perhaps you had better have an ambulance backed up to the sacristy door after the service, though, for I have some things to say to the Church Recalcitrant this evening." Chatworthy put his hand on his trusted friend's shoulder and smiled.

"Alfred, you are an intrigant," accused Boswell. "Go down to the library and look it up before the service."

"Won't be necessary, Bert, I caught it on the first bounce. It comes from the Latin *intrigare,* meaning, in the vulgar tongue, 'to get away with it.' Come, Kathleen," he said, turning to his wife, "we are expected at the Bombelberg's for dinner and we haven't much time."

Kathleen could be heard speaking to the Bishop as they left the parish hall, "Someday, Alfred, some one is going to pull the rope when your head is in the noose, where it is most of the time, anyway."

Dr. Bombelberg had been called to the hospital. Mrs. Bombelberg was in the kitchen, where she was joined by Kathleen. Alfred put "The Music Man" record on the hi-fi and leaned back in the lounger. He closed his eyes and drifted off into a musical limbo. . . .

"Ya got trouble, my friends, right here in River City . . . Why, sure I wear vestments, certainly, mighty proud, I say, I'm always proud to say it. I consider that the hours I spend in a surplice and stole are golden. Help you cultivate piety, a cool head, a pure heart. Did ya ever try to make a meditation for yourself in an alb and a chasuble? But just as I say, it takes judgment, brains and piety to click with a congregation . . . I say any boob can take and wear these brocaded vestments, and I call that pomp. I call that pageantry! The first big step on the road to degrada . . . I say, first it's a little fancy doings at the altar. Then genuflections, and the next thing you know, your minister is puttin' on a show in the parish church and listening to some out-of-town pastor hearing him tell about auricular confessions—not a wholesome consultation! No! But a deal where they set right down in a box! Like to see some stuck-up clergyman hearing confession? Make your blood boil? Well, I should say!

"Now friends, let me tell you what I mean. He's brought one, two, three, four, five, six new men in this here diocese . . . clergy that'll make the difference between a free church and a bund—with a capital 'B' and that rhymes with 'C' and that stands for Chatworthy!

"—and all year long you Blunderland people'll be payin' a tithe; I say you good folks'll be tithin'—tithin' away your food money, cigarette and show money, too! Read the Michigan tract! Never mind getting television, or a car each year, or the club dues paid! Never mind saving any money till you people are caught with an empty pocket book on Saturday night! And that's trouble. Oh yes, you got lots and lots of trouble. I'm thinking of the kids in the blue jeans, T-shirts, young ones peekin' in the parish hall window after school. Ya got trouble, folks right here in Blunderland, with a capital 'B' and that rhymes with 'C' and that stands for Chatworthy!"

"Now I know you folks are all the right kinds of parents. I'm gonna be perfectly frank. Would you like to know what kind of conversation goes on while they're loafing around the parish house? They'll be trying out thuribles, trying out charcoal, trying out incense, like spiky fiends. And braggin' how they're gonna smell up the church with incense! They'll come home using words like *oremus* and *dominus vobiscum* and *gloria patri!*

"One fine night they'll leave the house heading for the teacher's meeting—Oxford tracts and Latin rite and plainchant: shameless practice that'll drag your son and daughter to the arms of a spiky liturgical instinct! MASS-teria! Friends, the high-church brain is the devil's playground! Trouble. Right here in Blunderland. With a capital 'T' and that rhymes with 'C' and that stands for Chatworthy . . . Gotta figure out a way to keep the young ones e-van-gel-i-cal!"

Chatworthy came straight up out of the chair and looked wildly about him. The record had gone on to "Goodnight, my someone" as he recovered himself and shook off the pre-prandial twilight-mare. Unsteadily he got to his feet and made his uncertain way to the dining table. "The man that sang that sounded just like Codger," he ruminated.

Later that night with the opening service of Convention on his mind, and the "Music Man" still going through his head, Alfred fell asleep dreaming,

> A seventy-six voice choir led the big parade,
> While a hundred and ten white stoles dipped and swayed.
> There were double jointed crucifers and acolytes,
> And ample-bottomed celebrants of various kinds of rites. . . .

The following day, the Convention assembled for the Opening Service and Bishop's Charge. During the dying strains of the last verse of "The Church's One Foundation," a hymn that no one could trifle with, the Bishop of Blunderland ascended the pulpit, and during the 'Amen' reflected, "So, some think that the Bishop doesn't know the territory?" When everyone was settled, Alfred began his Charge to Convention.

"The Church's mission in mid-century is greatly in need of serious re-examination and subsequent adjustment to the hard facts of these latter days. This land in which we live was successfully colonized and developed by those who adapted to the conditions of life as it had to be lived if they were to wrench a living from nature. Those who stubbornly clung to the humid land ways of the East and Midwest in an attempt to twist nature's arm and force her to operate here as she did in other

172

"A seventy-six voice choir led the big parade."

climates, lost all they had and did not survive. Those of us who are native to this land know full well that the price of succeeding is to adapt. Adapt or perish became the cardinal rule of survival in a land that was not going to yield her increase except according to her nature.

"The same principle applies today in the life of the Church. We, too, must adapt ourselves to the deep spiritual needs of today's generation and meet them as the Church has always done when she has been aware and awake to her children's necessities. There are many demands upon the Church if she would meet the spiritual needs of this generation. Here, therefore, are the ten New Commandments for a Church that will face a disintegrating world and attempt to apply the healing power of the Gospel of Christ:

173

"First, the Church must place the faith and practice of our apostolic ancestors foremost in her interest, thought, and action among the people.

"Second, the Church must face the opposition between her God-centered demands and the demands of a modern society, whose ways and thinking are man-centered, and suffer the consequences, whatever these may be.

"Third, the Church must accelerate even more her teaching on the nature of God, and of man as creature and servant of God.

"Fourth, the Church's worship must consist in adoration of, and entrustment to, a God who is external to the worshippers and above things human.

"Fifth, the Church must realize that while foreign missions are of command; they are ridiculous unless every congregation sets out to do something about its own condition and its own community, first.

"Sixth, the Church and her congregations must cease all attempts to conceal from herself and the world the smallness of her achievement.

"Seventh, the Church must come to realize that the evangelizing of the world, involving the conformity of man's conduct to divine will, is the laymen's job: the Clergy exist to train and empower the laity.

"Eighth, the Church must insist not only on a better type of layman, but on one who will allow the clergy to be priests of God and not expect them to do the laity's work.

"Ninth, the Church must make it plain that she does not regard her properties, organizations, and enterprises as ends in themselves, but as means of restoring God's children to a right relationship with Him.

174

"Tenth, the Church must eradicate from her life and fabric all the left-overs from respectabilianism—especially rid herself of the curse of racism, and remove completely the idea that this Church is for the elect of the community and the world.

"The Church in America in our generation has been smothered by a discreet veil thrown over human sinfulness and over the supernatural power of God, and yet, through it all, we can see the Church begin to rise up from her deep sleep. In spite of the fact that a great many Churchmen have discounted miracles, relied on their own resources, and have denied the reality of God, the Church is beginning to move.

"There is still present among us an anxiety to please, instead of an eagerness to learn and a desire to teach. We are still trusting in our organizational and institutional capacities, but even so, new life is stirring.

"For the past hundred years, we have been largely occupied in turning the Christian religion into a loosely knit group of private chapels, which have been used as places to extend a morality, a social behavior, and a piously cultural way of life, tinged with local ceremonial additions—and all this with a growing neglect of the things of the Spirit.

"Much of our thought has in it the idea that as we ascend the ladder of good works, God is looking down from the top, waiting for us to arrive. Too many of our people suffer from the illusion that our aim is to make ourselves so lovable that God can't help Himself. We are still seeking too avidly for our own preservation at the cost of conformity, for the development of the organizational, for the desire to debate rather than to act, for the pedestrian in casual worship, and its sentimentalized morality. There isn't enough of the religious in the Church for the task. There is a way, however, that our world and our civilization can become humanized and the dignity of the human soul restored: the Church can again become truth-centered and God-centered. It can happen if enough rebels will pay the price. There must be a rising up of those who will seek for those things which just now the crowd does not seem able to understand.

"Even though I profess and work at being a Christian and a Churchman, I see the faintheartedness of those who constitute today on earth what God intends to be the Militant Body of Christ. I cannot forget how time after time in the past, God has raised up the Church out of impotence as great as that manifest today; I cannot forget how time after time, God has rescued her from cowardice, compromise, and organizationalism, and has sent her forth to salvage men from the ruin of the world, with the crowd about to overwhelm the Spirit; nor have I forgotten the cost of such restoration; this, the faithful have never refused, those numbered with the saints through the ages, the noble army of martyrs. The fire is coming, and I am genuinely confident that the Church's children will come to their senses in time and again accept the fire without flinching, and come out purged and refined as men and women of the Spirit.

"I do not deny that the Church at this moment may well be accused of being cowardly, complacent, conceited, and sycophantic. That condition must first be admitted and paid for. Until then the Church will continue, not to be hated, but to be ignored. The past is presenting its bill in our day. As over and over again in the past, this I know: God the Holy Spirit will come, lighting with flame as of fire, painful but purifying, coming like a rushing mighty wind, filling all the house. God send that day and soon."